ASTRO ADVENTURES

by DENNIS SCHATZ and DOUG COOPER

PACIFIC
SCIENCE
CENTER

This curriculum is the result of the combined talents of many past and present Pacific Science Center staff, especially: Vicki Fleming, Dara Hallman, La Verna Kashmir, and Ellen Polsky.

Art Direction, Design, and Illustrations:
Robert M. Brünz/RM Brünz Studio

Editing:
Christine White

Printing:
K&H Printers

Photo credits:
The Observatories of the Carnegie Institution of Washington, pp. 12, 14, 22
Dennis Schatz, slides 1-4
NASA, slides 5-18

NASA

Publication of *Astro Adventures* was made possible by a grant from NASA/Washington Space Grant at University of Washington. Pacific Science Center gratefully acknowledges their support.

Pacific Science Center
200 Second Avenue North
Seattle, Washington 98109-4895

CONTENTS

INTRODUCTION

WELCOME TO ASTRO ADVENTURES

We believe that the best way to teach and learn is through active involvement of the learner. For astronomy, this can be difficult, due to the challenge of making this topic tangible. This curriculum is designed to allow you and your students to use hands-on activities to investigate a variety of astronomy topics.

Our intention is for this to serve as a very flexible curriculum resource. The units may be taught in any order, or you may choose only to concentrate on those that are appropriate to your teaching situation.

We have designed *Astro Adventures* to include several features to assist in planning and using the activities with your students.

Unit Overviews will help in planning how to use each topic. In most cases, each activity is independent of the others in a particular unit. The order that we have chosen for the activities is one that seems to work well for our style of teaching. You may find, after reading through the activities, that a different order will work best for you.

The first four units are similar in arrangement, with the first activity of each unit designed as an open-ended activity. The purpose is to stimulate interest in the theme of the unit and to encourage students to want to learn more about the unit's topic. Most of the subsequent activities in each unit can be taught in any order. The fifth unit contains activities that may be used at any time during the course of study.

Advanced Preparation suggestions are meant to give information about tasks that need to be accomplished before starting the lesson with students.

A **Teacher's Note** appears in the middle of some of the activities. These notes are meant to communicate ideas about why the lesson is structured in a particular way and to assist the teacher with understanding the type of student responses being asked for at a particular point.

As you plan your course of study be sure to check the ideas listed in the **Subject Area Integration Suggestions**. These may allow you to stretch your astronomy study into other areas.

Many of the activities are purposely designed with open-ended tasks, problems, and challenges. Our goal is to encourage students to work together, using their problem solving skills to determine suitable solutions to these exercises.

These activities have been developed and used over many years with astronomy education programs at Pacific Science Center. The responses we have had from students and teachers in these programs have been very positive. Participants have learned much about the content of astronomy as well as developing essential problem solving and learning skills.

We hope that you and your students enjoy these astronomy adventures.

Dennis Schatz
Doug Cooper

ABOUT THE AUTHORS

Dennis Schatz is the Associate Director for Education of the Pacific Science Center. A research astronomer prior to his career in science education, Mr. Schatz has become a leader in science museum education and program development. He is active in science curriculum development, having published numerous articles and three science activity books for children.

Doug Cooper is the Supervisor of Teacher Education at Pacific Science Center. His experience as an elementary classroom teacher has provided him with insight into meeting the needs of both teachers and students when developing curriculum. Mr. Cooper has created program curriculum on such diverse topics as probability, whales, chemistry, lasers, muscles, ladybugs, and two of his favorites topics: science and children's literature.

✸✸✸

Pacific Science Center, in Seattle, Washington, is one of the nation's leading science museums, serving nearly 1.2 million people through on-site visits and outreach programs each year. Pacific Science Center is an independent, not-for-profit educational foundation dedicated to increasing the public's understanding and appreciation of science, mathematics, and technology through interactive exhibits and programs.

UNIT OVERVIEW

These activities allow your students to express what they already know about the moon, as well as gather information to expand their knowledge. As they explore lunar photographs in Activity One, the students will begin to make specific observations and inferences about the moon based upon their prior knowledge. Activity Two leads students to make specific observations of the moon as they consider what causes the phases, as well as developing the concept that the moon phases follow an observable specific sequence. This concept is reinforced during Activity Three as students explore the relationship of the earth, moon, and sun while modeling the moon's orbit. Activity Four explores the why, when, and how of solar and lunar eclipses.

A PLANNING CHART FOR MOON GAZING

ACTIVITY	TIME ALLOWANCE	WHEN TO START
Activity One *Predicting Phases and Features*	Approx. 45 minutes	Start activity on the day of a first quarter moon, or a couple of days before.
Activity Two *Observing Phases and Features*	Approx. 45 minutes Approx. 10 minutes	Same day as Activity One, or next day. Daily for one to four weeks.
Activity Three *Modeling Moon Phases*	Approx. 45 minutes	At the end of Activity Two.
Activity Four *Modeling Eclipses*	Approx. 30 minutes	After Activity Three.

MORE MOON GAZING

- Moon Background Information
- Subject Area Integration Suggestions
- Bibliography

PREDICTING PHASES AND FEATURES

Everyone has a mental image of the moon. Often this is a single image, like the full moon. This activity investigates students existing knowledge of the moon's appearance, making their observations in the following activities more meaningful.

CONCEPTS

The moon follows a specific pattern of phases. Observable characteristics can be used to identify features of the lunar surface.

OBJECTIVES

Students will:
- draw their mental image of the moon.
- infer the sequence of the moon's phases based on observations of lunar photos.

MATERIALS

Lunar Photographs
scissors
pencil
tape or glue
sheets of blank paper

PROCEDURE

Advanced Preparation:
Make copies of the Lunar Photographs for each work group of two or three students.

1. Distribute sheets of blank paper. Ask students to close their eyes and create a mental picture that answers this statement: "When I think of the moon it looks like this to me." Have them draw their mental pictures on the blank paper.

2. Have students compare their pictures. Discuss why the pictures may vary.
   Teacher's Note: You should not judge the appropriateness of each drawing, or students' reasons for their drawings. Use the drawings and information as clues to their conceptions of the moon.

3. Divide the class into small work groups of two or three students. Distribute copies of the Lunar Photographs, tape or glue, scissors, and a sheet of blank paper to each work group. Have students cut out the photographs. Their goal is to place them on the sheet of paper in the order they think they would see them if they observed the moon throughout several weeks. Allow 5 to 10 minutes for them to work with the photographs.

Teacher's Note: As each group completes its sequence, ask why the group chose its specific response. Do not judge the appropriateness of each sequence; rather, use the conversation to encourage students' deeper thinking and to give you a better idea of their understanding of lunar phases.

4. Once each group is satisfied with the order of the photos, students should tape or glue them to the blank sheet of paper. Have them number the pictures from one through six, in the order each would be seen. Be sure they indicate which way is up.

5. When all of the work groups have completed their photo sequences, have them move about the room to see the predictions of each group. Ask work groups to explain their reasoning for choosing the sequence they used. Encourage discussion of whether one sequence is more appropriate than another.
   Teacher's Note: It may be difficult, but this discussion should not lead to a conclusion about the most appropriate sequence. It should be used to set the tone for further discovery about lunar phases in the next activity.

6. Post the predictions on the bulletin board for reference during Activities Two and Three. During Activity Two, have students periodically review the photographs to determine whether they want to revise their predictions.
   Teacher's Note: If one carefully examines the lunar surface features, it is possible to determine the sequence in which the photos were taken— except the order may be reversed and the images upside down. At this point in the unit, you will not want to give away the answer to the sequence. Students will discover the appropriate sequence for themselves during Activity Two.

LUNAR PHOTOGRAPHS

Cut out each picture. Arrange them in the order you would expect to see the moon during the next several weeks.

PACIFIC SCIENCE CENTER

OBSERVING PHASES AND FEATURES

Activity One establishes an understanding of students' prior knowledge of moon phasing and provides a reason to further explore this phenomenon. Activity Two challenges the student to learn more in order to determine the most appropriate photo sequence of moon phases. In this activity, students observe the moon during a two-week to one-month period, record their observations, and compare them to their sequence of photographs from Activity One.

CONCEPT

The moon follows a specific pattern of phases that can be observed and recorded.

OBJECTIVES

Students will:
- make a daily record of moon observations.
- use their observations to refine their predictions of the moon's phases.
- use their observations to determine the sequence of lunar phases.

MATERIALS

Lunar Observing Record Chart
pencil
binoculars (optional)
clipboard or other firm writing surface

PROCEDURE

Advanced Preparation:
Make copies of the Lunar Observing Record Chart. Look in an almanac, daily newspaper, or on a calendar to determine when the first quarter moon will be visible for the month you are planning this activity. It is best to start this activity two or three days before the first quarter.

1. Begin this activity on an afternoon when the first quarter moon is visible in the sky. Students may not realize the moon is often visible in the daytime as well as at night. This will allow you to help students do some daytime observations during the early part of this activity. With your assistance, students will be able to use their skills to make nighttime observations.

2. Distribute copies of the Lunar Observing Record Chart. Tell students they have an opportunity to determine the sequence of the moon photos from Activity One by observing the moon over the next two to four weeks.

3. Explain how the Lunar Observing Record Chart is used:

   a. Go outside as a group and locate the moon. Record the date, time of the observation, and the shape of the moon. The pictures at the top of the Lunar Observing Record Chart will help students choose the most appropriate phase of the moon.

   Teacher's Note: If students ask what is meant by "waxing" and "waning", state that this will come in the next activity. A full explanation at this point will give away the results prematurely.

   b. Have students go out every clear day and repeat their observations. After the first observation, make a class activity of predicting what phase the moon will be in before the next observation.

   c. Post a classroom copy of the Lunar Observing Record Chart located on one wall of the classroom, where daily observations are summarized.

4. Students should work independently during the one to four weeks of observing, with periodic classroom updates on their observations.

5. As the students' observations progress, use their results to determine which of the sequences of lunar photos from Activity One is most appropriate. Several sequences are possible unless students know which part of the moon is at the top. If they do not realize this multiple possibility, you may need to point it out. Steer their discussion by suggesting that they look at the moon's surface features during subsequent observations to see which ones are near the top. This is a good time to introduce the different features visible on the moon, such as craters, maria, and rays.

GOING FURTHER

Advanced students may want to consider how their observations of the moon would vary if they lived in the Southern Hemisphere; for example, in Australia. This is a difficult problem for elementary level students, but a nice one which will encourage open-ended study.

Teacher's Note: Here is the most appropriate arrangement of the lunar photographs used in Activity One. The photo of the full moon in the background information can be used to determine correct orientation.

LUNAR OBSERVING RECORD CHART

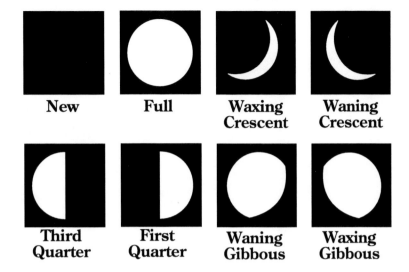

New	Full	Waxing Crescent	Waning Crescent

Third Quarter	First Quarter	Waning Gibbous	Waxing Gibbous

Directions: Find the moon in the sky. Record the date and time in the box corresponding to the date. Shade the circle to show the moon's appearance.

SUN	MON	TUE	WED	THUR	FRI	SAT
◯ Date ____ Time ____	◯ Date ____ Time ____	◯ Date ____ Time ____	◯ Date ____ Time ____	◯ Date ____ Time ____	◯ Date ____ Time ____	◯ Date ____ Time ____
◯ Date ____ Time ____	◯ Date ____ Time ____	◯ Date ____ Time ____	◯ Date ____ Time ____	◯ Date ____ Time ____	◯ Date ____ Time ____	◯ Date ____ Time ____
◯ Date ____ Time ____	◯ Date ____ Time ____	◯ Date ____ Time ____	◯ Date ____ Time ____	◯ Date ____ Time ____	◯ Date ____ Time ____	◯ Date ____ Time ____
◯ Date ____ Time ____	◯ Date ____ Time ____	◯ Date ____ Time ____	◯ Date ____ Time ____	◯ Date ____ Time ____	◯ Date ____ Time ____	◯ Date ____ Time ____

MODELING MOON PHASES

This activity allows students to use models of the sun, earth, and moon to discover why the moon phases occur.

CONCEPT

The observed phase of the moon is determined by its position relative to the earth and sun.

OBJECTIVES

Students will:
- be able to state the order of the moon's phases from one full moon to the next.
- demonstrate how the moon's position relative to the earth creates the phases.

MATERIALS

light bulb on a stand or clamp (or lamp with its shade removed)
extension cord
one Styrofoam ball or light colored sphere for each student (as model moon)
pencil and paper
darkened room

PROCEDURE

Advanced Preparation:
Collect enough Styrofoam balls to have one for each student. Be sure that there is plenty of space for students to stand and move about as they work through this activity. Check that the lamp or light bulb for the model sun works properly and that it can be placed in the front of the room where everyone can see it. The room will need to be completely dark for this activity.

1. Review the results of Activity Two, which showed that the moon goes through a sequence of phases. Work with the students to review the order of the phases from one full moon to the next.

2. Explain that to understand why the phases of the moon occur, students need to look at models of the moon, earth, and sun. Place the lamp in front of the room. Remind students of safety near the hot light bulb and electrical cord. Have students stand in a semicircle facing the lamp. Explain that the lamp represents the sun and that their head represents the earth, with their nose being their hometown.

3. Ask students to stand so it is noon in their hometown. If disagreement occurs, have them discuss this until it is agreed that noon is when their nose is pointed toward the "sun." Ask them to stand so it is midnight. They should turn so they face away from the "sun." Ask them to stand so it is sunrise and sunset. In order to stand properly, they will need to know their "earth" head rotates from right to left, with their right shoulders moving forward. Practice the ideas of sunrise, noon, midnight, and sunset until you feel that the students have a good understanding of these relative positions.

4. Distribute one Styrofoam ball moon model to each student. Have students stick a pencil into the ball to make it easier to hold and not interfere with their ability to observe the phases of the moon model. Have students hold the moon model at arm's length. Allow time for them to explore how the sun's light reflects off the model as they place their moons in different positions around their "earth" head.

5. Choose one of the lunar phases and ask students to find the position in the "moon's" orbit where that phase is visible. (First quarter is a good phase to start with.) Encourage students to compare their results and discuss differences. Ask one student who has the correct position to state why it is right. As the teacher, you can check for understanding by seeing if all of the students are standing in the same position.

6. Have students model the other phases; for example, full moon, third quarter, and new moon. As they learn where to hold the Styrofoam model for each phase of the moon, challenge them to determine the direction the real moon travels around the earth to create the phases in the correct order. (This can be demonstrated by moving the ball from right to left in orbit around the head.)

7. Allow time for students to experiment with the movement of the moon. Have them work together to draw a diagram of the moon's position in order to create each of the phases. Ask students to state what causes the phases of the moon. (The spinning earth—your head—makes the moon rise and set each day, but this does not affect the phase of the moon. The phases are caused by movement of the moon around the earth.)

8. Have students check their positions for the moon against those in the moon phases diagram that follows.

THE MOON AS SEEN FROM EARTH

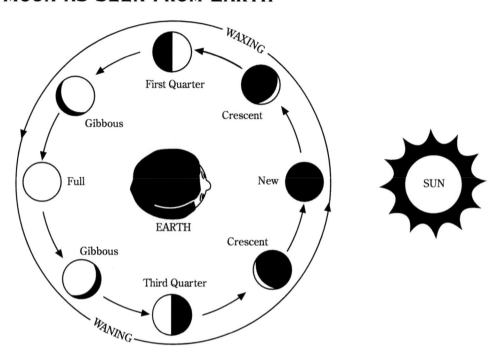

THE MOON'S POSITION RELATIVE TO THE EARTH AND SUN AS VIEWED FROM OUTER SPACE, ABOVE OUR SOLAR SYSTEM

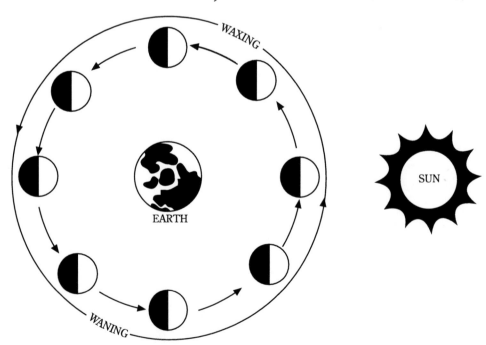

MODELING ECLIPSES

This activity explores why, when, and how often solar and lunar eclipses occur, using the earth, moon, and sun models of Activity Three.

CONCEPTS

Eclipses are caused by a predictable alignment of the earth, moon, and sun. Different alignments create lunar and solar eclipses.

OBJECTIVES

Students will:
- distinguish between lunar and solar eclipses.
- model how lunar and solar eclipses occur.
- predict when an eclipse is most likely to occur.
- determine whether more people can see a total lunar or total solar eclipse.

MATERIALS

light bulb on a stand or clamp (or lamp with its shade removed)
extension cord
one Styrofoam ball or light colored sphere (as model moon)
pencil and paper
two hula hoops

PROCEDURE

Advanced Preparation:
Read the eclipse information at the end of this unit for a more thorough understanding of eclipses.

1. Ask students if they know the definition of an eclipse and the difference between a solar eclipse and a lunar eclipse? Explain that this activity will help them understand the difference between these two types of eclipses and why they occur.

2. Set up the equipment as it was used in Activity Three, with students in a semicircle facing the lamp. Have them move the moon ball in orbit until it completely blocks their view of the lamp. Explain that when the moon is positioned between the earth and the sun, and it blocks the sun, it produces a solar eclipse. Students can remember this by thinking of the view of the sun as being clipped off. Have students position themselves so that the view of the full moon is clipped off by the earth's shadow. Ask them to tell you what phase the moon must be in to produce each type of eclipse.

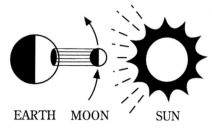

Total Solar Eclipse
Moon must be in new phase. Only people in a small region on earth where the moon's shadow falls can see the total solar eclipse.

EARTH   MOON   SUN

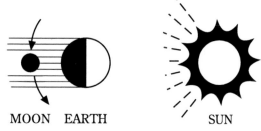

MOON   EARTH   SUN

Total Lunar Eclipse
Moon must be in full phase. All people on the night side of the earth can see lunar eclipse.

3. Now that students know what causes eclipses, ask them to predict how often there should be solar and lunar eclipses, and whether more people get to see a total solar eclipse, or a total lunar eclipse. Give them time to work with the moon ball model before guiding them to the answers.

4. Although solar and lunar eclipses occur with equal frequency, a person is less likely to see a total solar eclipse than a total lunar eclipse. Ask students to take partners. Have one partner hold the moon ball to produce a solar eclipse. Have the other person look at the shadow of the moon falling on the face of his/her partner. Ask students to consider this question: if the student's head were the earth, from what part of the earth could people see the solar eclipse? Have the partner hold the ball to produce a lunar eclipse. Ask if more people will see a lunar eclipse or a solar eclipse. Generate a list of predictions for how often solar and lunar eclipses should occur, along with reasons for the answers.

5. Hold two hula hoops over your head, as shown in the illustration, to show the relationship of the path of the sun and the moon *as seen from earth* (your head). The inside hoop is the orbit of the moon, with the moon making one complete revolution each 29.5 days. Have one student use their moon model to follow the path of the moon around the earth. Discuss the route the moon takes as it orbits the earth.

6. The outer hoop represents the sun's apparent path as seen from earth, with the sun appearing to go around the earth once a year. (Although the earth actually goes around the sun, our view from earth makes the sun appear to go around the earth.) Have one student trace the path of the sun around the hoop. Ask how it differs from the moon's path. Where do the moon and sun have to be to produce an eclipse? (At the crossing points.)

7. Use the students' knowledge of how often the moon and sun are at the crossing points to determine how often eclipses occur (see Background Information).

BACKGROUND INFORMATION

THE MOON

The moon is earth's only natural satellite. Its regular orbit creates a sequence of phases. The moon is visible above the horizon at different times of the day, depending on its phase (e.g., the full moon is above the horizon from about sunset to sunrise, first quarter from about noon to midnight, and third quarter from about midnight to noon).

The moon progresses through a full sequence of phases approximately every 29.5 days. The phase it exhibits is due to its position in the sky relative to the sun and the earth. *Waxing* and *waning* are terms that describe how the moon's phases are changing. A waxing moon is when the moon's bright portion of the moon is getting bigger, as in "wax builds up on your car." A waning moon is when the bright portion of the moon is getting smaller, as in "waning away."

Several features of the lunar surface are visible from earth. Craters are circular features ranging in size from one inch to more than 100 miles in diameter. Craters are formed when meteoroids collide with the moon. Meteoroids are large rocks traveling through space at thousands of miles per hour. The energy in the collision blasts a large hole with a ridge of rock around its outer edge. Many craters also have mountain peaks in their centers. The craters Tycho, Copernicus, and Kepler are easily seen during a full moon.

The force of the impact often splashes up rock that spreads across the surrounding area in long, thin rays extending away from the crater. This is especially visible in the Crater Tycho, where some rays of ejected material extend for more than 1,000 miles.

Maria (Latin for "seas") are the large dark features on the moon. Astronomers believe they formed several billion years ago just after the moon was created, when it still had a thin crust. Large meteoroids hit the moon with such force that they broke through the crust, and molten lava from below filled shallow basins on the surface. The lava cooled into the large flat areas we see as maria. The maria are darker than the surrounding areas because the rock is basalt, a volcanic rock that is darker than the material making up the surrounding mountains.

Mountains are especially easy to see around the edges of most maria. The mountains probably rose over four billion years ago, shortly after the moon's crust formed, when most of the moon was still hot and molten. As the material cooled, the moon shrank slightly, resulting in buckling of its outer layer. This pushed rocks up, to form the mountainous features we see today. The lack of an atmosphere means that almost no erosion occurs, the moon's mountains have changed little since they were formed.

MOON FEATURES

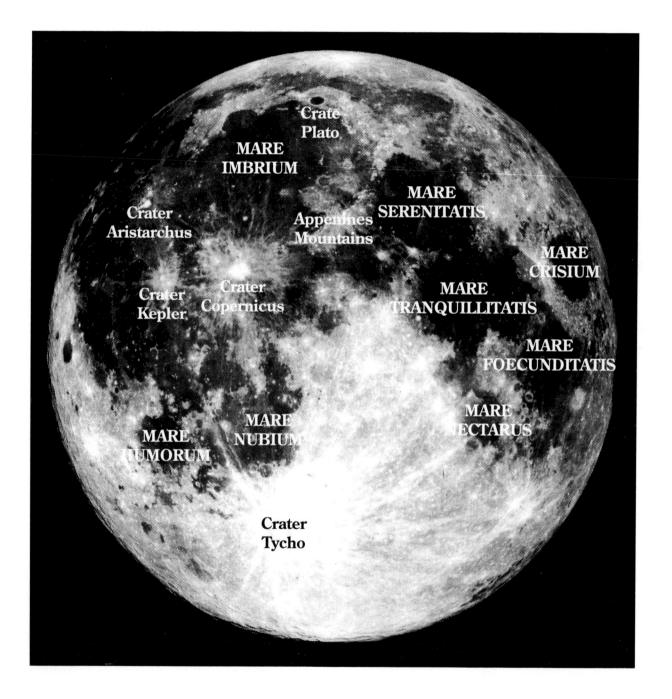

Crater
Plato

MARE
IMBRIUM

MARE
SERENITATIS

Crater
Aristarchus

Appenines
Mountains

MARE
CRISIUM

Crater
Kepler

Crater
Copernicus

MARE
TRANQUILLITATIS

MARE
FOECUNDITATIS

MARE
NUBIUM

MARE
NECTARUS

MARE
HUMORUM

Crater
Tycho

ECLIPSES

Eclipses can occur only when the moon is in certain phases. For a total solar eclipse, the moon must come directly between the earth and the sun, which means that the portion of the moon facing away from the earth is sunlit. Observers on earth see a new moon.

For a total lunar eclipse, the earth, moon, and sun must again be in a straight line, but now the moon and sun must be on opposite sides of the earth. This can occur only when the moon is full. A reasonable conclusion is that a solar eclipse and a lunar eclipse should occur every 29.5 days. However, this does not correspond with our everyday experience, which indicates that eclipses are rare events.

To understand how often eclipses occur, we must examine more closely the path of the sun and moon. If the two orbits were exactly aligned, then lunar and solar eclipses would occur every 29.5 days. However, the two orbits are at slight angles to each other, so most of the time the moon passes above or below the direction of the sun or the earth's shadow. In order for there to be an eclipse, the earth, moon, and sun must be in a straight line. This occurs only when the moon and sun are at the crossing points of their orbits—where the two hoops cross each other in the model. Although the moon is at these crossing points approximately twice a month, the sun is at the intersections only twice a year.

When the sun is at a crossing point, the motion of the moon is sufficiently quick so both a lunar eclipse and a solar eclipse occur within about 14 days of each other. Approximately six months later there is another pair of eclipses when the sun is located at the other crossing point.

On rare occasions, the sun stays close enough to the crossing point long enough so that three eclipses occur within a month. For example, if the moon passes in front of the sun (a solar eclipse) just as the sun reaches the intersection of the two paths, a lunar eclipse occurs about 14 days later. Another solar eclipse would then occur 14 days after that, just as the sun is leaving the crossing point.

The complex motions of the earth, moon, and sun actually cause the time between eclipses to be slightly less than six months. This means that on extremely rare occasions, when the first eclipse occurs in early January, there are three sets of eclipses in one year. This happened in 1982, when there were four solar eclipses and three lunar eclipses.

Observers on about one-half of the earth can see a total lunar eclipse, but only a small number of people get to experience a total solar eclipse. The path of the moon's shadow as it crosses the earth's surface is less than 300 miles wide. On the average, a total solar eclipse occurs only once every 360 years for a single location on the earth. A total solar eclipse is also the one time that most earthbound viewers can see the beautiful solar atmosphere called the solar corona. Viewing a total solar eclipse is often a once-in-a-lifetime event and well worth traveling long distances to see.

Here is a list of where total solar eclipses will occur during the next 25 years:

November 3, 1994	South Pacific Ocean South America South Atlantic Ocean Indian Ocean
October 24, 1995	Middle East India Southeast Asia South Pacific Ocean
March 9, 1997	Soviet Siberia Arctic Ocean
February 26, 1998	Pacific Ocean South America North Atlantic Ocean
August 11, 1999	North Atlantic Ocean Europe Middle East India
June 21, 2001	South Atlantic Ocean Southern Africa Madagascar Indian Ocean
December 4, 2002	South Atlantic Ocean Southern Africa Indian Ocean Australia

March 29, 2006   Atlantic Ocean
Northern Africa
Middle East
Soviet Union

August 1, 2008   Northern Canada
Greenland
North Atlantic Ocean
Soviet Union
China

July 22, 2009   India
China
South Pacific Ocean

July 11, 2010   South Pacific Ocean
Southern South America

November 13, 2012   Australia
South Pacific Ocean

March 20, 2015   North Atlantic Ocean

March 9, 2016   Indonesia
Borneo
Pacific Ocean

August 21, 2017   North Pacific Ocean
United States
North Atlantic Ocean

SUBJECT AREA INTEGRATION SUGGESTIONS

References to the moon a bound in daily life. These suggestions may help you and your students broaden your scientific study of the moon, by exploring its relation in other curricular areas.

MATH

- Weigh several objects using a spring balance or scales. To find the weight of the objects on the moon, multiply the earth weight by .16. How much would students weigh on the moon?

- Determine the maximum and minimum number of full moons that could occur in one year. Would this change in a leap year? How many times could a "blue moon" occur in one year? (A blue moon is when two full moons appear in the same month.)

SOCIAL STUDIES

- Where could you go to see the next eclipse?

- List famous people who have explored the moon or discovered things related to the moon.

- Research different cultures and the stories that they have created about the moon.

- How have other cultures used the phases of the moon to create a calendar or to show the passage of time?

- The September full moon was known as the harvest moon by early American pioneers. How did it get this name? Research names for all of the 12 moons of the year. How were their names derived?

LANGUAGE ARTS

- Pretend you are living in an ancient civilization, and are creating a mythology to explain why the moon's phasing occurs. Write the story of your myth.

ART

- Design a moon community.

- Design and create a flip book of the moon's changing phases.

- Find an outdoor place where only the moonlight is shining. Use crayons to draw a picture. Observe differences in the way the colors appear in moonlight versus how they appear in sunlight or artificial indoor light.

- Find paintings showing the moon at night. How has the artist represented the moon? What colors does the artist use to represent a scene lit by moonlight?

MUSIC

- Make a list of songs with the moon in them.

READING

- Search the library for stories, poems, and folktales in which the moon plays a part of the story. Read them to each other.

HEALTH

- What products and health care materials were designed as part of NASA and the original space race to the moon?

PHYSICAL EDUCATION

- Do creative movements with your body to show moon phasing.

BIBLIOGRAPHY

For more information about the moon, see the following books, as well as the resources in your local library.

FOR STUDENTS

Cooper, Henry S.F., *Apollo on the Moon and Moon Rocks*, Dial Press, 1970.
Darling, David J., *The Moon — A Spaceflight Away*, Dillon Press, 1985.
French, Bevan, *The Moon Book*, Penguin Books, 1977.
Simon, Seymour, *The Moon*, Collier Macmillan, 1984.

FOR ADULTS

Brewer, Bryan, *Eclipse*, 2nd ed., Earth View, Inc., 1991.
Cherrington, Ernest H., *Exploring the Moon Through Binoculars and Small Telescopes*, Dover, 1984.
Hokey, Thomas A., *The Book of the Moon*, Prentice-Hall Press, 1986.
Kitt, Michael, *The Moon: An Observer's Guide for Backyard Telescopes*, Kalmbach Books, 1992.

UNIT OVERVIEW

Though the sun is 93 million miles away, its importance to our planet is unequaled by any other astronomical object. These activities allow your students to observe interesting features of the solar surface, investigate the sun's role in our concept of time, and locate direction. In Activity One, students build sun clocks to visually investigate the relationship between the sun's apparent daily motion across the sky and our concept of passing time. Activity Two has students using the sun clocks to determine cardinal directions. Activity Three provides students with a safe technique for viewing sunspots and their changes on the solar surface.

A PLANNING CHART FOR SUN WATCHING

ACTIVITY	TIME ALLOWANCE	WHEN TO START
Activity One *Making a Sun Clock*	Approx. 30 minutes to assemble Approx. 45 minutes to test Several 5 to 10 minute observing sessions	Two or three class sessions on a sunny day.
Activity Two *Using a Sun Compass*	Approx. 40 minutes	One class session on a sunny day.
Activity Three *Projecting an Image of the Sun*	Approx. 45 minutes the first day Approx. 5 to 15 minutes daily for three to four days in a row	Three to four class sessions of sunny days.

MORE SUN WATCHING

- Sun Background Information
- Subject Area Integration Suggestions
- Bibliography

MAKING A SUN CLOCK

Our concept of time is based on the motion of the sun. In this activity students construct sun clocks. They are challenged to determine the correct orientation needed for the sun clock to function. Keeping track of the sun's shadow with the sun clock helps students visually understand the relationship between the sun's motion and our concept of time.

CONCEPT

Our concept of time is based upon the apparent motion of the sun.

OBJECTIVES

Students will:
- construct pocket sun clocks.
- determine local noon using the sun clocks.
- make observations about the passing of time using their sun clocks.
- explain the relationship between the motion of the sun and our concept of time.

MATERIALS

Pocket Sun Clock pattern (for your location)
cardboard slightly larger than the sun clock (file folders, index cards, etc.)
string, 20 centimeters (7 inches) long
glue
chalk or pencil
scissors
tape

PROCEDURE

Advanced Preparation:
Make a copy of the Pocket Sun Clock pattern for each student. (Be sure to use the pattern appropriate to your state.) If possible, copy the sun clock pattern on heavy paper, tagboard, or card stock. (If this is not available, duplicate the pattern on regular paper and have the students glue their patterns to heavier weight paper. Old file folders or large index cards are good materials.)

1. Distribute copies of the appropriate Pocket Sun Clock pattern for your location. Have students cut out the rectangular pattern.

2. Students then cut the short notches at each end, as indicated on the Pocket Sun Clock pattern. They should fold the clock along the dotted line on the pattern, making sure the hour lines are to the inside.

3. Have students take approximately 20 centimeters (7 inches) of string, place one end through one of the notches on the sun clock, and tape it to the back of the clock.

4. Have them stretch the other end of the string through the notch at the other end of the sun clock. The string should be adjusted so it is tight when the two panels of the clock are at a 90-degree angle. Have students tape the string's end to the back of the sun clock.

5. Ask the students to decide what they would need to make their clocks work. Have them predict if the sun clocks must be in any special position to register the correct time.

   Teacher's Note: The students should discover that the clocks must always face the same way—south. This is a good problem solving activity, so give them plenty of time to discover the required positioning of the clocks.

PROPERLY ASSEMBLED SUN CLOCK

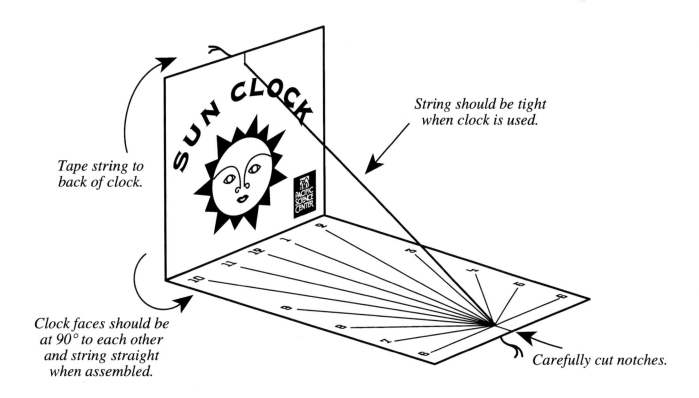

String should be tight when clock is used.

Tape string to back of clock.

Clock faces should be at 90° to each other and string straight when assembled.

Carefully cut notches.

a. Before going outside to use the sun clocks, check the time on a clock or watch. If it is daylight saving time, subtract one hour to give standard time.

b. Once students have the correct standard time, take them outside to a sunny location where there is a flat surface. Be sure the location will be in the sun for at least the next half hour. The string of the sun clock must be taut. Students should rotate the clocks until the shadow of the string reads the correct time. Ask students if there is more than one way to orient the clock to read the correct time.

c. Have students use a pencil or piece of chalk to draw a box around the base of the clocks so they can remember the sun clock's orientation. They should put their initials inside the boxes so they can find their clock's location when they make the next observations.

d. Return to the classroom and ask students to predict what they will need to do to their sun clocks so they read correctly when they check the time in 15 to 45 minutes. Will they need to change the clocks' orientation? How much, if any, will they need to move them? Will more than one orientation work?

e. After 15 to 45 minutes, the students place their sun clocks back in the spots marked earlier and determine what must be done to read the correct time.

6. Discuss how to correctly orient the clocks. Did all orientations work? Is there anything special about the direction the string faces on the sun clocks?

7. After students have developed a set of instructions for correctly positioning the sun clocks, they need to remember some other details that help in their operation:
   a. Use the clock on a level spot, away from buildings and trees which create shadows.
   b. Choose an accessible location.
   c. The first time the sun clock is used, line up the string's shadow to give the same time as a clock or watch. (Don't forget to adjust for daylight saving time, if it is in effect, by subtracting one hour from the time on the clock or watch.)
   d. Draw an outline of the sun clock on the surface to get an accurate future readings.

POCKET SUN CLOCK

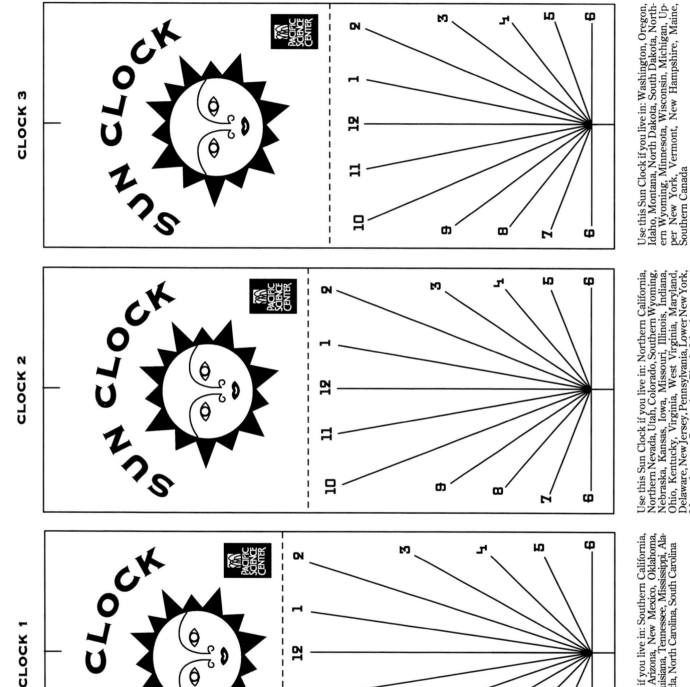

CLOCK 3

SUN CLOCK

Use this Sun Clock if you live in: Washington, Oregon, Idaho, Montana, North Dakota, South Dakota, Northern Wyoming, Minnesota, Wisconsin, Michigan, Upper New York, Vermont, New Hampshire, Maine, Southern Canada

CLOCK 2

SUN CLOCK

Use this Sun Clock if you live in: Northern California, Northern Nevada, Utah, Colorado, Southern Wyoming, Nebraska, Kansas, Iowa, Missouri, Illinois, Indiana, Ohio, Kentucky, Virginia, West Virginia, Maryland, Delaware, New Jersey, Pennsylvania, Lower New York, Massachusetts, Connecticut, Rhode Island

CLOCK 1

SUN CLOCK

Use this Sun Clock if you live in: Southern California, Southern Nevada, Arizona, New Mexico, Oklahoma, Texas, Arkansas, Louisiana, Tennessee, Mississippi, Alabama, Georgia, Florida, North Carolina, South Carolina

USING A SUN COMPASS

Being able to correctly orient the sun clock in Activity One is important in using it to tell time. A correctly aligned sun clock can also tell cardinal directions. After students become comfortable reading time, this activity may be introduced. It will let them explore how to use the sun clock as a compass.

CONCEPT

The sun's position can be used to determine cardinal directions.

OBJECTIVES

Students will:
- tell time using a sun clock.
- determine cardinal directions (north, south, east, and west) using a sun clock.
- follow a set of directions using the sun clock as a compass.
- create a map based upon a set of directions.

MATERIALS

Pocket Sun Clock (created in Activity One)
watch
pencil or chalk
drawing paper
cardboard X's or other marker (one for every two to three students)
Compass Riddle

PROCEDURE

Advanced Preparation:
This activity uses the sun clock built in Activity One. Determine an appropriate playing area for the outdoor portion of this activity. Make several large X's on construction paper or cardboard for the riddle described in the middle of this activity. Make copies of the riddle for students. Students should be reminded that it is not safe to look directly at the sun.

1. While in the classroom, ask students to think about how the sun clock could be used to find direction. Allow some time for them to explore this possibility with their sun clocks.

2. Write their suggestions on the board, directing the discussion toward the following conclusions:
   a. You need to know the time from a watch or clock to know that the sun clock is properly aligned, adjusting for daylight saving time.

b. A correctly aligned sun clock faces south. By knowing one cardinal point, other directions can be determined.

3. On a sunny day, go outside with sun clocks. Ask students to hold their sun clocks level and rotate them until they show the correct time. The sun clocks are now facing south, with the strings running in a north-south direction. Have students point in the direction you call out to them. If they are facing south, north will be behind them, east to the left, and west to the right. Try several different directions until you are confident that students know them.

4. Place cardboard X's about 20 feet apart in an open area with little shade. Divide students into small work groups of two or three. Have the groups stand at each X.

5. Give each group a copy of the following riddle. They will have to use their sun clock as a compass, in order to solve it.

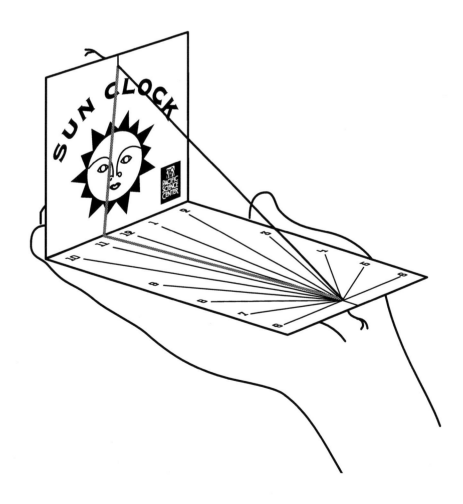

COMPASS RIDDLE

A treasure is buried where these directions lead you. Use your sun clock to follow the instructions below to tell you where you should dig:

a.   Take 5 steps north
b.   Take 5 steps east
c.   Take 5 steps north
d.   Take 10 steps west
e.   Take 5 steps south
f.   Take 10 steps east
g.   Take 5 steps south
h.   Take 5 steps west

Teacher's Note: If students successfully follow the directions, they will end at the spot from which they started. Advanced students can devise their own directions for other teams to follow. Some may want to experiment with median directions such as northeast or southwest.

6. After students have worked outdoors and followed the directions to the "treasure," have them draw maps that accurately portray the cardinal directions and are correctly aligned with them. What playground features might be added to provide additional interest and references on their maps?

7. Students may wish to create their own treasure map directions.

PROJECTING AN IMAGE OF THE SUN

Sunspots are the most conspicuous features observed on the solar surface. This activity demonstrates a safe method for examining sunspots and how they change.

> **Important:** Do not look directly at the sun through binoculars. Permanent eye damage can occur without any feeling of pain.

CONCEPT

The sun has sunspots that move and change over time.

OBJECTIVES

Students will:
- record sunspot observations over several days.
- compare sunspot records and the changes that occur over time.
- demonstrate appropriate safety precautions related to observing sunspots.

MATERIALS

binoculars
tripod
masking tape
scissors
piece of cardboard, one-foot-square
white sheet of paper on a clipboard or other firm surface
clear light bulb (optional)
clamp lamp or lamp without shade (optional)

PROCEDURE

Advanced Preparation:
Assemble the binoculars and tripod so they will be ready to use. You may want to practice focusing the binoculars on a clear light bulb. The light bulb's filament will shine through the binoculars and be projected on a white sheet of paper in the same manner as sunspots.

> **Teacher's Note:** The first time you do this activity, it should be as a demonstration for the entire class. Later observations can be made by students who you know will be able to observe safely.

1. Before going outside, tape the lens cover to the opening of one side of the binoculars. (Make sure not to tape over the focusing control of the binoculars or the adjustment controls of the tripod.) If there is no lens cover, tape paper over the opening so no light can enter that side of the binoculars.

2. Extend the tripod to its full length and tape the binoculars securely to the tripod.

3. Cut a hole in the center of the cardboard the same size as the binoculars opening you did not cover. Slip the cardboard over the opening and tape it in place.

4. Go outside and point the binoculars in the approximate direction of the sun. RE-MEMBER, UNDER NO CIRCUMSTANCES LOOK DIRECTLY THROUGH THE BINOCULARS AT THE SUN. Loosen the control knobs on the tripod. Watch the ground behind the binoculars as you adjust them to point directly at the sun. A very bright area of light will project on the ground when you have the binoculars pointed directly at the sun. (It takes practice to get the binoculars aimed at the sun. One good indicator of how close you are to having them aligned is to watch its shadow on the ground. The shadow will be as small as possible when the binoculars are aimed at the sun.)

5. Once the bright area of light is on the ground, tighten the tripod control knobs. Hold the sheet of white paper about two feet behind the binoculars so the area of light falls on the paper. The area of light is an image of the sun, but it may be out of focus. Adjust the focus knob on the binoculars until you get a sharper image of the sun on the paper. Sometimes you may see only part of the sun because the binoculars are not aligned exactly with the sun. If this occurs, carefully adjust the tripod so the full sun comes into view on the paper.

6. As you examine the image of the sun, you will notice that it is moving across the paper. In a few minutes, the sun will go out of view completely and you will need to adjust the tripod to bring it back into view. This is an interesting phenomenon for students to observe and hypothesize why it occurs. (This occurs because the earth is rotating, causing the sun to appear to move across the sky throughout the day.) You need to regularly realign the binoculars to keep up with the sun's changing position in the sky.

7. While looking at the sun's image on the piece of paper, carefully examine the entire solar surface for any dark spots. If you are not sure whether the spot is on the sun, in the binoculars, or on the paper, lightly tap the binoculars. If the spot moves with the sun's image, it is a sunspot. Record the total number of sunspots you see. If the sunspots are large, make a drawing of them on the paper for comparison on another day.

8. Repeat your observations daily, using a new sheet of paper each day to record the number of spots and to compare the drawings of large sunspots.

BACKGROUND INFORMATION

THE SUN

Our sun appears to be the largest and brightest of the stars that can be seen with the naked eye. This illusion is produced by the nearness of the sun to the earth. In actuality, our sun is one of the smaller and fainter of the stars.

The sun is about 93 million miles from the earth. Having a diameter at its equator of approximately 860,000 miles, the sun is about 109 times the diameter of the earth. If the sun were a hollow ball, more than a million earths could fit into it.

The sun is not a solid body like the earth, but a huge ball of very hot gases. Like other stars, the sun gives off a tremendous amount of energy. This energy is produced from a nuclear reaction taking place deep inside the sun. It is believed by astronomers that hydrogen atoms in the sun combine to form helium atoms. When this process takes place, some of the hydrogen is converted into vast amounts of energy. This continuous reaction creates a surface temperature of about 6,000°C (10,800°F).

The surface of the sun has violent storms that are indicated by dark areas known as sunspots. Sunspots are the facial blemishes of the sun. These dark regions on the solar surface appear in generally predictable patterns and locations, growing larger over a few days to a few months and then fading away. Some sunspots are round, while others have very complex patterns. All of the larger spots have dark regions embedded in a lighter surrounding area. Some spots seem to remain unchanged for days, while others change shape and size dramatically in one day.

Sunspots develop where high concentrations of magnetic field inhibit the flow of energy, producing cooler regions compared to the surrounding areas. These cool areas are still hot enough to melt lead (4,000°C/7,000°F) but, as the cooler areas emit less light, they are darker than their hotter surroundings (6,000°C/11,000°F).

The diameter of the sun is 109 times that of the earth so, even though a sunspot appears small, it usually becomes noticeable to the earthbound observer only when it is about the size of our planet.

During certain years, such as in 1986, the sun is almost free of blemishes. But five to six years later it is covered with sunspots. In another five to six years, the sun is again blemish-free. This 11-year cycle between times of high sunspot activity has been documented for over 300 years.

During observations over a number of days, sunspots appear to move slowly across the surface of the sun. The sunspots actually do not move significantly from where they erupt. Their motion is due to the sun's rotation on its axis which carries them across the face of the sun. The surprising result from years of observation is that material near the equator of the sun moves faster than regions closer to its poles. A sunspot at the sun's equator takes only 26 days to make a complete turn around the sun. Unexpectedly, sunspots at the sun's poles, a much shorter distance, take 37 days to make a complete turn around the sun.

SUN CLOCKS

The sun has been used to tell time for centuries. Sundials and other sun clocks read local time. Astronomers define local noon in the Northern Hemisphere as the time when the sun is exactly in the south. Noon is also when the sun is at its highest point above the horizon each day. Since the 12 o'clock noon line on the sun clock in this curriculum is directly below the string, the string must be oriented exactly on the north-south line to read properly at noon. (Note: these directions are true north and south as determined by the stars, and not magnetic north. These can differ by as much as 30 degrees.)

Sundials read local time, while clocks give standard time or daylight saving time. The continental United States is divided into four time zones. Everyone agrees to say it is the same time everywhere within a given time zone, even though the sun is not exactly in the same position. It is actually noon first at the eastern edge of a time zone and then, about an hour later, noon at the western edge of a time zone.

The boundaries of the time zones are not always straight, in order to minimize communication problems between cities. In some cases, the boundary is moved hundreds of miles east or west to keep an entire state in the same time zone. In other cases, the state is divided between two time zones because of geographic features such as a river. If a common, standardized time was not in effect, it would be confusing and difficult to calculate time in another city when we need to telephone someone there.

SUBJECT AREA INTEGRATION SUGGESTIONS

The significance of the sun is found in many aspects of our lives. These suggestions may help you and your students broaden your study of the sun, by exploring its relation in other curricular areas.

MATH

- Design a sun clock that will accurately read the half hour and quarter hour.

- Set up a number of objects on a sunny part of the playground. Measure the length of the shadows over time.

SOCIAL STUDIES

- From a list of cities, determine the time difference between each city as well as the difference between each city and your hometown. What geography points of interest are in time zones east or west of yours? In the Northern and Southern Hemispheres?

- Research the history of the sundial. Tell where and when it was invented, and give different versions of telling time by the sun.

- Look for myths and stories from different native cultures. How do the stories help you understand more about that culture and its geographic location?

LANGUAGE ARTS

- Write stories using themes: The Day I Lost My Shadow
                                  Journey to the Sun
                                  The Day the Sun Didn't Shine

- Write a newspaper article on the discovery and/or invention of the sundial and its ability to tell time. Include the who, what, where, when, and why of good journalism.

- Read *Peter Pan* and discuss how his shadow was an important part of the story.

ART

- Create a clock or design a watch.

- Make a sundial wristwatch. Design an ad campaign for selling this new fashion item.

MUSIC

- Create a list of songs that have lyrics or titles related to the sun, such as sunshine or shadows.

READING

- Find stories that use the sun, shadows, or sundials as elements of the story. Share short stories with other members of the class. Here are two books for young children: *Anno's Sundial* by Mitsumasa Anno
  Arrow to the Sun by Gerald McDermott

- Read stories to younger students. Discuss parts that are real—based on science as currently accepted.

HEALTH

- Report on looking at the sun and eye damage, suntans, and sunburns. Find out how these topics are being researched by scientists.

- Invite a pharmacist or doctor to speak on reactions the sun could have on medications that people may need to take.

PHYSICAL EDUCATION

- Play shadow tag.

- Create a sundial on the playground using people's bodies.

BIBLIOGRAPHY

For more information about the sun, see the following books, as well as the resources in your local library.

FOR STUDENTS:

Darling, David J., *The Sun — Our Neighborhood Star*, Dillon Press, 1985.
Ridpath, Ian, *The Universe: The Sun*, Schoolhouse Press, 1986.

FOR ADULTS:

Frazier, Kendrick, *Our Turbulent Sun*, Prentice-Hall Press, 1983.
Friedman, Herbert, *Sun and Earth*, Scientific American Library, W.H. Freeman, 1986.
Wentzel, Donat G., *The Restless Sun*, Smithsonian Institution Press, 1989.

UNIT OVERVIEW

People have probably gazed at stars in the night sky since the beginning of time and wondered what they were. The activities in this section allow your students to use stars as signposts in the sky. In Activity One, students view a pattern of stars in order to design their own constellation and create stories, much as cultures around the world have done for centuries. Activity Two has students building and using a star finder to locate different constellations. Activity Three uses the star finder from the previous activity as a map to locate other celestial, deep space objects. In Activity Four, students explore the relationship between the changing position of constellations during the night and the passage of time.

A PLANNING CHART FOR STAR FINDING

ACTIVITY	TIME ALLOWANCE	WHEN TO START
Activity One *Create a Constellation*	Approx. 20 minutes to create constellations Approx. 15 minutes to create stories Approx. 20-30 minutes to share stories	Anytime.
Activity Two *Star Finding with a Star Finder*	Approx. 20 minutes to assemble Approx. 15 minutes to practice	Anytime.
Activity Three *Finding Deep Space Objects*	Approx. 15 minutes to assemble Approx. 15 minutes to practice	After completing Activity Two.
Activity Four *Star Clocks*	Approx. 15 minutes to assemble Approx. 15 minutes to practice	After completing Activity Two.

MORE STAR FINDING

- Star Background Information
- Subject Area Integration Suggestions
- Bibliography

CREATE A CONSTELLATION

For centuries, people in all parts of the world have looked at the stars. The patterns remind them of familiar objects or characters from stories. Different cultures have associated mythological creatures and stories with different constellations of stars.

This activity allows students to create their own constellations and stories from a given pattern of stars, and compare them to what other cultures have seen in the same pattern.

CONCEPT

Constellations are stars that have been grouped to suggest important cultural objects, animals, story characters, or people.

OBJECTIVES

Students will:
- define the term *constellation* as a pattern made from a group of stars.
- use a common pattern of stars to design a constellation.
- write a short myth about their constellation.

MATERIALS

Create a Constellation pattern
overhead transparency of Create a Constellation pattern
pencil
blank paper

PROCEDURE

Advanced Preparation:
Make copies of the Create a Constellation star pattern sheet for each student. Make an overhead transparency of the Create a Constellation pattern.

1. Ask students to name some constellations they've heard of or observed. Discuss with them how they think the constellations got their names. Define the term *constellation.*

2. Distribute copies of the Create a Constellation pattern to each student. Have students observe with the star pattern from any and all possible directions.

3. Have students draw figures or objects using some or all of the stars in the star pattern.

4. Have students write brief stories about their figures and how they came to be found in the stars.

5. Share student-created stories and drawings to emphasize how different people see different figures in the same pattern. The students' stories and drawings can be posted on the bulletin board or put together in a class book.

6. Relate to the students that just as different people in the class saw different figures in the star patterns, so have various cultures when looking at the stars in the night sky. The pattern of stars on the Create a Constellation sheet represent an actual star pattern visible in the night sky.

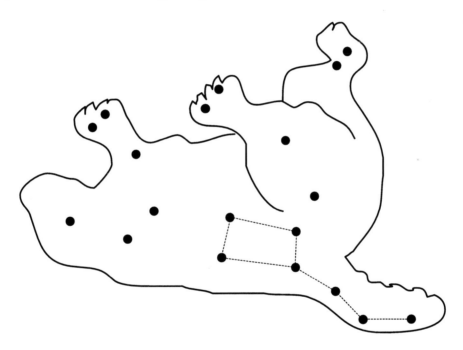

7. Using the overhead projector, show students where the Big Dipper is found in the Create a Constellation star pattern. This pattern is actually the constellation of Ursa Major. (Astronomers do not consider the Big Dipper as its own constellation because it is part of a larger group of stars.) If possible, draw the rest of the illustration of the bear.

8. Read stories from different cultures based upon this same star pattern. Students may wish to illustrate these cultural stories using the Create a Constellation pattern sheet.

9. Have students research other constellations. Try to find different cultural stories and myths for the same star group.

URSA MAJOR MYTHS FROM AROUND THE WORLD

GREEK

The god Zeus often changed himself into various animals to carry out his plans upon mortal women. To hide the nymph Callisto from the wrath of his wife, Hera, Zeus changed her into a bear. This saved Callisto from Hera's anger, but introduced her to other dangers—now earthly hunters could take her for a common bear and attempt to kill her. One hunter, named Actas, saw the bear Callisto, drew his bow and prepared to shoot her. Now this was an awful situation, made more terrible by the fact that Actas was the son of Callisto. To prevent Actas from killing his mother, Zeus placed them together in the sky as the Big and Little Bear. According to Ovid, Zeus swung the creatures by their tails to do this, and that accounts for the fact that both Big and Little Bears happen to have abnormally long tails.

According to another Greek myth, the sky is made of soft, pliable glass. Nailed to this glass is a bearskin, held in place by seven nails. The seven points make up the Big Dipper.

In another tale, Zeus became angry at a poor earthly bear, picked it up by its tail, twirled it over his head, and tossed it into the sky.

To Homer, this constellation was both a bear and a "wain" (a wagon). He placed the bear upon the shield of Achilles, described in detail in one of the books of the *Iliad*.

IROQUOIS INDIANS

Once upon a time in a strange and distant land (New York State), some Indians were chasing a bear through the forest. The Indians ran into three giants who, angered by the chase, attacked and killed all but three of the Indians. Suddenly, the three surviving Indians and the bear were transported into the sky, where the chase continues to this day. The bear is formed by the four stars in the cup of the dipper, and the three stars in the handle represent the three Indians. The one closest to the bear carries a bow to shoot the bear, the next one carries a pot to boil the bear in, and the last Indian carries wood to light the fire. The Indian who carries the pot is the star Mizar, and his pot is Mizar's faint companion star, Alcor.

ZUNI INDIANS

For most of the year, the great bear guards the western lands from the frozen gods of the north. In the winter, however, the bear goes into hibernation, leaving the land to be ravaged by the frozen breath of the ice gods. The bear wakes in spring—his growling is to be heard in the spring thunder—and drives the frozen gods back to the north, where they belong.

HOUSATONIC INDIANS

The big bear hibernates every winter in the cave known to the Greeks as the Corona Borealis. Three Indian warriors find the bear asleep and attack it. The bear wakes up in agony and takes off in a mad dash across the sky, with the three Indians in hot pursuit. It is the tableau of this chase that we see when we gaze into the sky—the four stars on the cup form the bear and the tail stars are the three Indian warriors. The chase lasts for quite some time; finally, around October, the Indians catch up with their quarry. The lead Indian takes his spear and stabs the bear. Although the creature doesn't die, it bleeds profusely and the blood falls out of the sky and onto the leaves of the trees. And that's why leaves turn bright red in the fall.

BASQUE

Once upon a time in the land of the Basques, a man was robbed of two oxen by two thieves. Enraged, the man sent his servant, his housekeeper, and his dog out to chase the thieves and recover the oxen. After a long wait, the man lost his patience and chased after the thieves himself. As punishment for his impatience, the man was taken up into the sky with all the other elements of the story. The first two stars in the cup of the dipper are the two oxen, the other two stars are the two thieves; in the handle of the dipper are the servant, the housekeeper, and the master, who is the final star. The dog is the faint star Alcor.

CHINESE

Chinese astronomers called this constellation the "Jade Balance of Fate." Chinese peasants called it the "Grain Measure."

ARABIAN

The Arabians saw a coffin and mourners in this constellation. The coffin is formed by the four stars of the dipper's cup; the mourners, sons of the deceased, are the three stars in the handle. The three stars here are following the North Star seeking vengeance, for it is that star that killed their father.

GERMAN

To the Germans, who had much first-hand experience with bears, this constellation was not a bear. It was a "Grosse Wagen" (big wagon).

ENGLISH

King Arthur was said to live in the portion of the sky marked by the Big Bear. This conception became transferred in later times to "King Arthur's Chariot" slowly circling the pole. The Irish refer to this group of stars as "King David's Chariot."

CREATE A CONSTELLATION

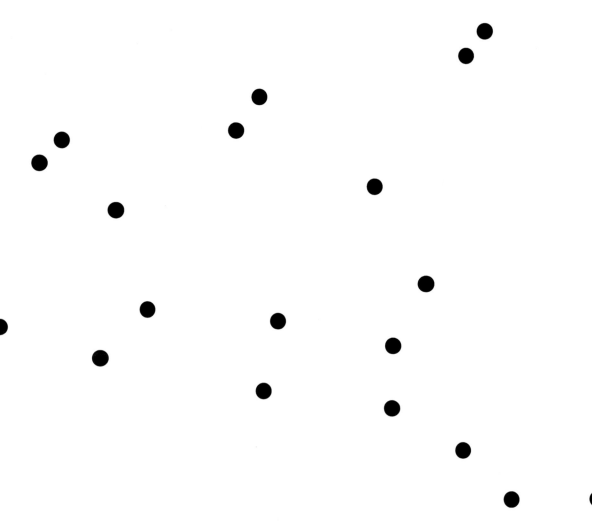

STAR FINDING, Activity One
© 1994 Pacific Science Center

PACIFIC
SCIENCE
CENTER

STAR FINDING WITH A STAR FINDER

A star map of the night sky helps locate different constellations in the same way a road map helps locate different cities on the earth. In this activity students construct a rotating star finder to find the constellations visible in the night sky throughout the year.

CONCEPTS

Constellations remain fixed in their relative position to each other.
Constellations appear in the sky at different times, due to the earth's daily rotation and seasonal orbit around the sun.

OBJECTIVES

Students will:
- construct a star finder.
- identify constellations using a star finder.
- observe the effect of seasonal changes when viewing constellations.

MATERIALS

Star Finder patterns: holder, and two constellation wheels
scissors
file folders (one and one-half per star finder)
glue
stapler

PROCEDURE

Advanced Preparation:
Make enough copies of the Star Finder patterns so each student can make their own. Creating a sample ahead of time will help them understand what the final product should look like.

CONSTRUCTING THE STAR FINDER

1. Distribute one manila folder and the Star Finder Holder pattern to each student.

2. Have students glue the holder pattern to the front of a manila file folder, with the east-south edge of the holder along the fold of the file folder.

3. Have them cut out the star finder as indicated on the pattern, including the central oval. They should staple the front and back together by placing staples exactly on the staple lines shown on the front of the Star Finder Holder.

4. Distribute copies of the constellation wheels and one-half of a manila folder to each student. Glue one of the constellation wheels to one side of the manila folder. Have them cut it out, then glue the other constellation wheel to the back. This technique makes it easier to line up the circle of the two wheels. It is not possible to align the dates on the two wheels, nor is it important for them to be aligned.

5. Have them insert the star wheel between the pages of the holder so the simple star field appears through the oval opening. Once the star wheel is completely inserted, test turn the star wheel to be sure it moves freely. Check to see that the black line under the dates on the star wheel approximately lines up with the edge of the star finder cover showing the time of day.

USING THE STAR FINDER

1. Before going outside to use the Star Finder, practice using it in the classroom. Have the students align the current date on the wheel with the time indicator on the holder. The following set of questions and directions will help them become familiar with the star finder.
   a. Assume you are going to observe at 9:00 p.m. tonight. What constellations are visible?
   b. Turn the dial until it is set for 11:00 p.m. tonight.
      1. Which constellations are visible?
      2. Which constellations were visible at 9:00 p.m., but are no longer visible at 11:00 p.m.?
      3. Which horizon are disappearing constellations closest to?
      4. Which constellations are visible at 11:00 p.m., but were not visible at 9:00 p.m.?
   c. Turn the dial until it is set for 5:00 a.m., just around sunrise.
      1. Which constellations are still visible that were up at 9:00 p.m.?
      2. Describe the motion the constellations follow from 9:00 p.m. to 6:00 a.m.
      3. Rotate the dial one complete turn, which represents a 24-hour day. Which constellations never go below the horizon?
   d. Hold the star finder over your head so that the "North" designation on the star finder is pointing north. The stars showing in the oval opening are those that can be seen overhead at the time and date set on the star finder. The edge of the oval represents the horizon. Stars near the edge of the oval are low on the horizon. The center of the oval is the point directly overhead when you look up in the night sky. This point is called the zenith. Stars near the center of the oval will be high overhead when you are observing.

e. Now you are ready to go star finding in the night sky. A small flashlight or penlight will help you read the star finder at night. Red plastic, red construction paper, or a red balloon, over the front of the flashlight will allow you to read your star chart by the red light, but will not reduce your ability to see faint stars in the sky.

Teachers Note: Have students practice using their star finders, pointing to where they would expect to find specific constellations.

2. The simple star field shows the bright stars visible in the major constellations. These stars are easily found, especially when viewing from a city where the many lights make it difficult to see faint stars. Once students are experienced at finding the bright stars on this side of the star wheel, they can flip the star wheel over and attempt to find the fainter stars and constellations. Some of these will not be visible until observed from a location away from city lights.

3. Once students become familiar with some of the brighter constellations, they can use them as guides to find your way around the sky. For example, they can use the two outer stars of the Big Dipper's cup to help find the North Star. Have them devise their own technique to use the stars to find other constellations.

STAR FINDER HOLDER

PASTE ONTO FOLDER, ALIGNING THIS EDGE WITH FOLDED SPINE OF FOLDER. THEN CUT ALONG EDGE OF STAR FINDER, BUT DO NOT CUT FOLDED EDGE!

STAPLE

EAST

5 AM 4 AM 3 AM 2 AM 1 AM 12 11 PM 10 PM 9 PM 8 PM 7 PM

NORTH

STAR FINDER

TO USE, TURN THE STAR WHEEL UNTIL THE CURRENT DATE LINES UP WITH THE TIME YOU WISH TO OBSERVE. HOLD THE STAR FINDER OVER YOUR HEAD SO "NORTH" ON THE STAR FINDER IS FACING NORTH. THE STARS SHOWING IN THE OPENING ARE THOSE THAT CAN BE SEEN OVERHEAD.

CUT OUT WHITE OVAL (THIS SIDE OF FOLDER ONLY).

STAR FINDER

PLACE THIS SIDE ALONG FOLDING EDGE OF FOLDER.

SOUTH

WEST

STAPLE

STAPLE

PACIFIC SCIENCE CENTER

STAR FINDING, Activity Two

STAR WHEEL
COMPLEX STAR FIELD

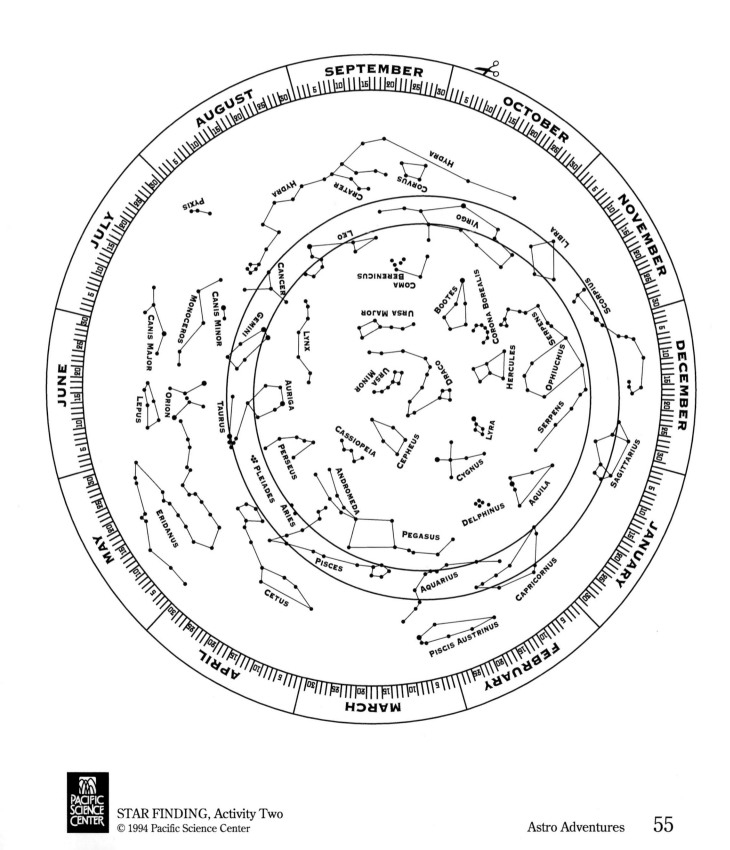

STAR WHEEL
SIMPLE STAR FIELD

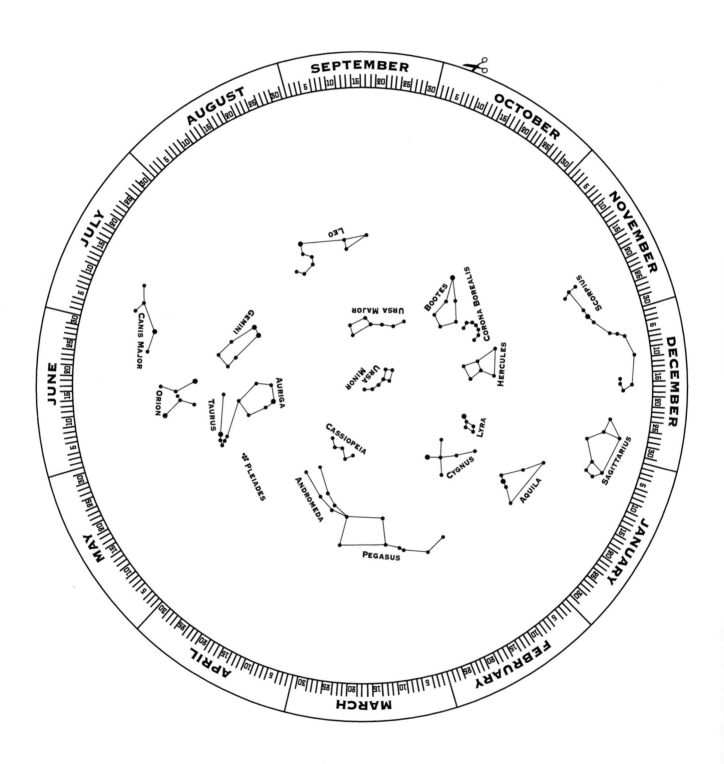

STAR FINDING, Activity Two
© 1994 Pacific Science Center

PACIFIC SCIENCE CENTER

FINDING DEEP SPACE OBJECTS

Constellations are not the only objects that can be found using a star finder. There are several deep space objects located near specific constellations. These include star clusters, nebulas, and other galaxies. This activity allows students to find deep space objects using their star finders and an additional wheel.

CONCEPT

Constellations can be used as reference points to find other celestial objects.

OBJECTIVE

Students will:
- use constellations to locate other celestial objects in the night sky.

MATERIALS

Star Finder from Activity Two
Deep Space Objects wheel patterns
one-half file folder for each student
glue
binoculars
flashlight (covered with red plastic if possible)
clear night sky

PROCEDURE

Advanced Preparation:
Copy the patterns of the Deep Space Objects star wheels for each student.

1. Distribute copies of the Deep Space Objects wheel patterns and one-half of a manila folder to each student. Have them glue one of the wheels to the folder, cut it out, and then glue the other wheel to the back. Using this technique makes it easier to line up the circle of the two wheels.

2. Have students insert the constellation side of the Deep Sky Objects wheel into the Star Finder Holder. Have them set the star finder for the time and date they wish to observe. Interesting objects are identified by the circles on the map. The drawings on the back side of the star wheel show how the objects should look through binoculars.

3. For the greatest success in locating the fainter objects, students should observe from a location with a clear night sky. They should also be as far from city lights as

possible on a night when the moon is not too full. Students should allow their eyes to become "dark-adapted" to see fainter objects. This may take several minutes. If possible, have them cover their flashlights with red plastic or paper so their eyes will stay dark-adapted when they use the flashlight to read the star finder. From earth, deep sky objects will appear as fuzzy spots of light, even through binoculars.

DEEP SPACE OBJECTS LOCATION WHEEL

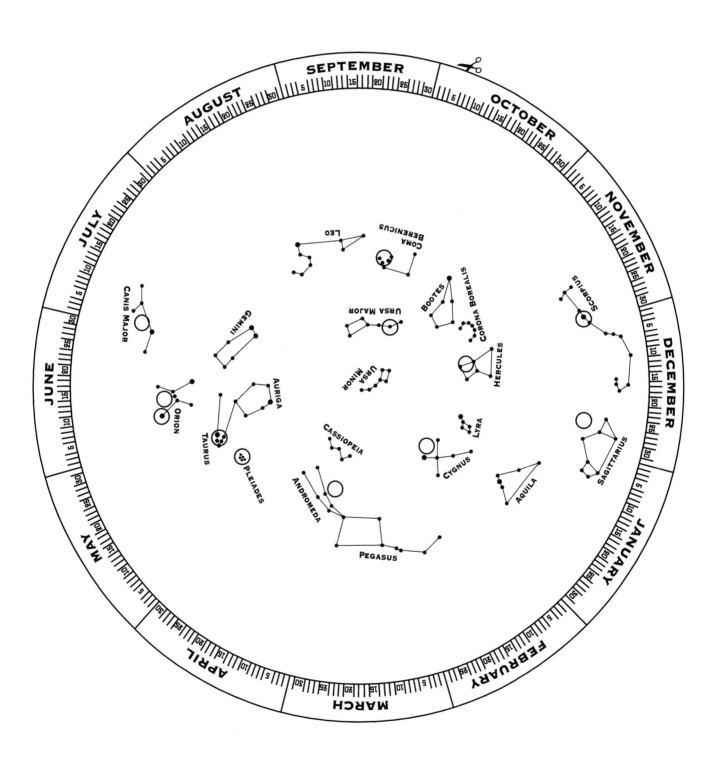

Deep Space Objects Wheel

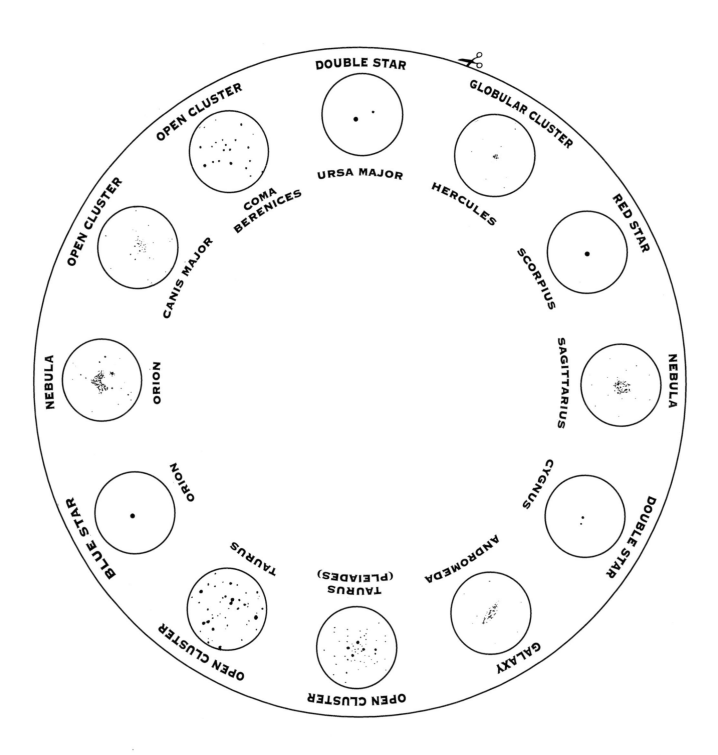

STAR FINDING, Activity Three
© 1994 Pacific Science Center

STAR CLOCKS

Our daylight concept of time is based on the motion and position of the sun. In this activity students are challenged to tell time at night with a star clock. They will determine the correct orientation needed for the star clock to function. Keeping track of the positions of constellations with the star clock helps students visually understand the relationship between the constellations' changing positions and our concept of passing time.

CONCEPT

The motion and position of constellations can be used to tell time.

OBJECTIVES

Students will:
- construct star clocks.
- determine local time using a star clock.
- make observations about the passing of time using their star clocks.
- explain the relationship between the motion of the stars and our concept of time.

MATERIALS

Star Clock pattern
Star Finder from Activity Two
large cardboard model of constellations of the star clock (optional)
paper fastener
scissors
glue

PROCEDURE

Advanced Preparation:
Make copies of the Star Clock pattern for each student. You may wish to create a large classroom version of the constellation section of the star clock to use as a teaching tool.

1. Ask students to tell you the time. Have them explain how they got that information. Ask how people long ago might have told time. What instruments could they use? (Take suggestions: for example, using the stars, using the sun, dripping water, or pouring sand.)

2. Ask students to describe how a person might tell time at night before watches and clocks were invented. Try to steer their discussion toward including ideas about stars and changing star positions.

3. Have students take out their star finders. Ask them to set their star finders for the position of the stars at 10:00 p.m. tonight, using the simple constellation field. Allow time for them to observe the position of the stars and constellations. Reset the star finder for 4:00 a.m. Ask students to describe the constellation differences they notice between these two settings. Discuss their observations and conclusions that stars are found in different positions at different times. (This is due to the daily rotation of the earth.)

4. Distribute copies of the Star Clock pattern and paper fasteners. Have students cut out the pieces and assemble their star clocks by putting the disk with the words "The Time Is" on top of the disk with the months. A paper fastener through the center of both disks holds them together.

5. Refer students back to their star finder, remind them that the positions of stars are different at different times. Explain to them that the star clock is a simplified star finder that can be used to tell time at night.

6. To use a star clock have students face the northern night sky, holding the star clock so the current month is at the top of the circle. They should turn the black disk until the outline of the Big Dipper lines up with the Big Dipper's position in the sky. (A large version of the black disk can help students practice accurately aligning the constellations of their clocks.) Ask students to tell the time by reading their star clocks. **Teacher's Note:** If it is daylight savings time students need to add one hour to their star clock reading.

7. To practice using the star clock, have each student select a time to leave on a trip to the Andromeda Galaxy and set their clocks. Carefully observe the position of the constellations; then, using the large classroom model, rotate the model. When the model matches the positions each of the students have selected on their star clocks, they should each make a ringing sound like an alarm clock. Since students have selected different times, be prepared for alarm clock sounds at different times.

8. The star clock can be used two different ways. It can use the position of the stars to tell what time of night it is, or it can tell what position the Big Dipper will be in at a specific time, which may make it easier to find in the night sky. Remind the students that they must always be facing the North Star when using the star clock. Challenge them to try to use their clocks tonight at home.

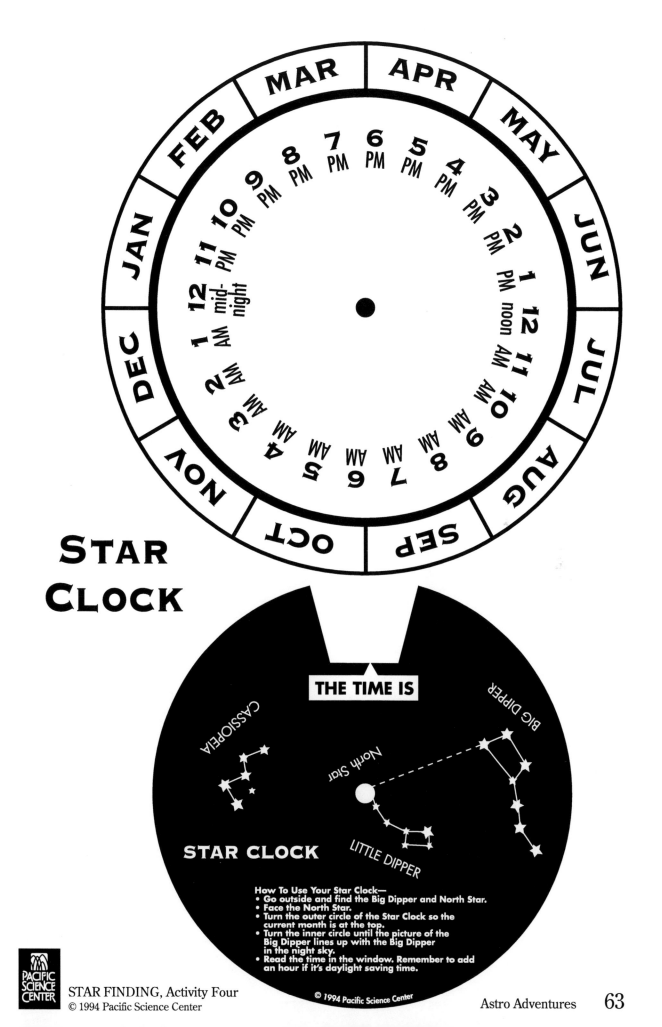

STAR CLOCK

THE TIME IS

STAR CLOCK

How To Use Your Star Clock—
- Go outside and find the **Big Dipper** and **North Star.**
- **Face the North Star.**
- Turn the outer circle of the Star Clock so the current month is at the top.
- Turn the inner circle until the picture of the **Big Dipper** lines up with the Big Dipper in the night sky.
- **Read the time** in the window. Remember to add an hour if it's daylight saving time.

PACIFIC SCIENCE CENTER

Background Information

The Stars

The sun is earth's closest star. It has provided scientists with a greater understanding of what distant stars may be like.

Stars, like our sun, are giant balls of gas held together by gravity. Stars may be thought of as tremendous thermonuclear reactors. The extremely high temperatures at the star's center fuses hydrogen atoms together, producing helium and releasing large quantities of energy. This energy ultimately reaches the star's surface where it is released as various types of radiation, including radio waves, infrared, and the visible light we see. These radiation products provide many opportunities for scientists to study and understand more about stars. Based upon their investigations, astronomers group stars into a variety of categories, including size, temperature, chemical composition, brightness, and relative distance from earth.

The visible color of the stars is an indicator of their temperature. Cooler stars (2,000°C/3,600°F) are red, while very hot stars (50,000°C/90,000°F) are blue. The constellation of Orion, visible in the winter months, contains the blue star Rigel and the red star Betelgeuse. Using a spectroscope (a tool that breaks the visible light from a star into its component colors) to analyze the light of a star, astronomers have been able to determine the specific chemical elements that compose individual stars.

Since ancient times people have used the constellations of the night sky as indicators of direction, as well as signals for the passing of the seasons. Astronomers use constellations as guideposts to find and observe deep space objects, such as galaxies, double stars, star clusters, and nebulas.

Some stars appear as single stars until viewed with binoculars. Then one discovers they are actually two stars, so close together that the unaided eye cannot separate them. A few of these double stars actually revolve around each other, but most are extremely far apart, with one much closer to earth than the other. They appear near each other because they are located in approximately the same direction from us.

From earth the stars appear to remain in fixed positions. Some of these positions have become the familiar patterns we call constellations. Our familiar constellations exist only from earth's viewpoint. If the same groups of stars that form constellations were seen from a different position in our galaxy, they would not form the familiar patterns we know.

Many people believe that there are an unlimited number of constellations. In a manner of speaking, this statement is true. Constellations are simply patterns of stars that people have agreed to call by the same name. Often the pattern of the stars creates a familiar image to the people agreeing upon a constellation's shape. Astronomers, on the other hand, have officially "recognized" only 88 constellations. This was done in 1920 by the International Astronomical Union which fixed the shapes and names of constellations seen in the skies of both the Northern and Southern Hemispheres.

Over 7,000 stars of the Milky Way Galaxy can be seen by the unaided eye from earth. Powerful telescopes reveal billions of additional stars that form our galaxy, and yet scientists believe there are millions, or perhaps billions, of stars in our galaxy that we cannot see, even with our most sophisticated equipment. Looking beyond our galaxy we see billions of other galaxies, all composed of millions or billions of stars. No one knows how many stars may exist.

SUBJECT AREA INTEGRATION SUGGESTIONS

These suggestions may help you and your students broaden your scientific study of the stars, by exploring its relation to other curricular areas.

MATH

- Use tangrams or other geometric shapes to create the shapes of constellations on grid paper. Calculate the areas of the different constellation shapes.

- Create a measuring system that will allow students to measure the distances between constellations as they are viewing the night sky. One example might be the number of fists from one constellation to another.

SOCIAL STUDIES

- Research the names of various constellations. What are the origins of the constellation names? How do the names of constellations seen in the skies over the Northern Hemisphere compare to those of the Southern Hemisphere?

- Research stories from different cultures that describe the same constellation. For example, what are the different stories for the constellation we call Orion?

- Find the geographic location of the cultures mentioned in the Ursa Major myths of the Create a Constellation activity. Plot their locations on a map. What geographic elements do these cultures share?

- Research how different cultures throughout time have created navigation systems based upon the stars. What similarities and differences did various cultures devise for using the stars to find their way?

LANGUAGE ARTS

- Search out well-known phrases that relate to stars. Analyze their meanings in terms of popular culture, then analyze their meanings from an astronomer's point of view and determine why they are not possible. For example, consider the phrase "Catch a falling star and put it in your pocket."

- Design and publish a classroom book of myths based upon student observations of various constellation star patterns. These could be the myths from the Create a Constellation activity, or a different set of star patterns.

- Write and illustrate an original story about a favorite constellation.

ART

- Illustrate the Create a Constellation ideas for the classroom book.

- Draw giant versions of the constellations, including their mythical illustrations. Create a classroom planetarium, using the star finder to correctly place the constellations on the ceiling and walls of the classroom.

- Using small foil balls, string, and a cardboard box, design a three dimensional model of a constellation as seen from the earth. How might we see this group of stars if we could view it from a different perspective, such as from below or from the side?

MUSIC

- Research and listen to songs that refer to stars in their titles or lyrics.

READING

- Research and read other cultural myths about different constellations.

- Learn and share poetry in which stars are mentioned in the titles or text. Analyze what the poets may have been thinking or feeling.

PHYSICAL EDUCATION

- Work in cooperative teams to create the shapes of constellations with the bodies of the teams.

- Work in teams to create the shapes of constellations using shadows.

BIBLIOGRAPHY

For more information about the stars, see the following books, as well as the resources in your local library.

FOR STUDENTS

Asimov, Isaac, *The Birth and Death of Stars*, Dell, 1991.
Branley, Franklyn M., *Star Guide*, Crowell Jr. Books, 1987.
Darling, David J., *The Stars: From Birth to Black Holes*, Dillon Press, 1987.
Ridpath, Ian, *The Universe: The Stars*, Schoolhouse Press, 1988.
Simon, Seymour, *Stars*, William Morrow and Co., 1986.

FOR ADULTS

Kaler James, *Stars*, Scientific American Library, W.H. Freeman, 1992.
Monroe, Jean G., and Williamson, Ray A., *They Dance in the Sky — Native American Star Myths*, Houghton Mifflin Co., 1987.
Weiss, Malcom E., *Sky Watchers of Ages Past*, Houghton Mifflin Co., 1982.

UNIT OVERVIEW

The planets of our solar system are one of the most intriguing topics of study for students. The activities in this unit will help students understand more about the unique characteristics of individual planets. They will also gain an understanding of the techniques astronomers use to study the planets, as well as some of the obstacles they face. Activity One focuses upon observations of Earth and comparisons that help understand other planets. In Activity Two, students conduct an in-depth study of one planet and design a creature that could successfully live on that planet. Activity Three and Activity Four focus upon the relative size of the planets and the vast distances between them. Inspiration for composing music is the theme of Activity Five.

A PLANNING CHART FOR PLANET PICKING

ACTIVITY	TIME ALLOWANCE	WHEN TO START
Activity One *Planet Picking*	Approx. 60 minutes	Any time.
Activity Two *Invent an Alien*	Approx. 20 minutes for initial assignment Approx. 7 to 10 days for research Approx. 3 to 5 days for alien display Approx. 5 to 10 minutes for each presentation	Works best after completing Activity One.
Activity Three *Scaling the Solar System*	Approx. 2 days	Any time.
Activity Four *Race to the Planets*	Approx. 2 days	Works best after completing Activity Three.
Activity Five *Music of the Spheres*	Approx. 15 to 20 minutes to listen to student selections Approx. 45 to 60 minutes for Holst section	Works best after completing Activity Two.

MORE PLANET PICKING
- Planets Background Information
- Subject Area Integration Suggestions
- Bibliography

PLANET PICKING

Many students find studying the planets in our solar system the most interesting part of astronomy. This activity encourages students to identify the similarities and differences among the planets by examining a number of planetary photographs. This introduction to the planets leaves the students eager to know more about the individual planets.

CONCEPT

Astronomers base inferences about planetary features upon observations of the earth.

OBJECTIVES

Students will:

* compare specific similarities and differences among the planets by examining various features visible in photographs.
* identify types of features found on planets by classifying the photographs into groups, using a classification scheme of their choice.
* infer planetary features based upon earth observations.

MATERIALS

Planet Picking Photos (one set of 18 per four to six students)
magnifiers (one or two per group)
Planet Picking slides
slide projector
slide tray
slide descriptions

PROCEDURE

Advanced Preparation:
Using the Planet Picking slides as a master, copy enough photo sets for the class to work in groups of four to six. Load slides into slide tray in correct position.

1. Distribute the photographs to groups of four to six students. Supply each group with one or two magnifiers to help them closely examine the features in the photographs. Ask each group to classify the photographs into a number of categories based on a scheme of its choiceJupiter.

    Teacher's Note: If students ask how many categories they should have, tell them that it is up to them, based on traits they choose to use for the categories. Some students will also want to know what is shown in certain photographs. Avoid giving answers at this point. Encourage them to discuss possible ideas.

2. Facilitate throughout the classroom. As teams complete their groupings, discuss with them their reasoning behind how they grouped the photographs. Encourage them to try different classification schemes. If time allows, encourage students to continue this process for as long as they are examining and discussing the photographs.

3. Once students are done, ask several groups to explain their classification schemes to the rest of the class. Select a variety of schemes for presentation. Students often think that there is only one right classification scheme for this activity, as well as thinking that there is only one way that scientists might classify objects in general. This is an excellent opportunity to discuss how a collection of objects can be classified in many different ways, depending on the traits chosen for making the categories.

4. Use the Planet Picking slides to analyze the 18 planet photographs. Begin by discussing specific features found in the slides of the earth. Discuss the observations of these earth-based photographs, progressing to the earth-from-space photographs.

   Ask:
   • what white features might be (snow, clouds).
   • what blue or blue-green features could be (water, sky, tree-covered mountains).
   • what tan or brown features can be (desert, beach).

   Have students identify these features in the first four photos. Share the slide description information as the students discuss each slide. Use the next five photos to have them identify what they are seeing from space.

   Teacher's Note: The immediate goal is not for students to be able to produce the right answer, but to go through the reasoning process that a scientist would use while examining these photographs. Extensive discussion should be allowed, based on the background knowledge of the students and the information available from looking at the photographs. Information you present about the photographs should occur only after extensive discussion among the students. The goal of the activity is to base planetary inferences upon similar observations made on earth. Due to the nature of other activities in this unit, try not to give away all of the details about each planet.

5. Show slide 10, the Mars slide. Ask students to determine the general terrain on Mars, using the colors observed (red = desert, white = polar caps). Examine the images of the Martian features in the next two slides and compare these to similar earth features (volcano and riverbed).

6. The craters visible on Mars can then be used as a lead-in discussion of similarities to the Moon and Mercury, shown in the next two photographs (low density atmosphere and resulting lack of erosion allows craters to remain visible for millions of years.)

7. Complete the analysis of the remaining images, being sure to highlight the items given in the following descriptions of the slides.

DESCRIPTIONS OF PLANET PICKING SLIDES

1) Pacific Science Center with the Olympic Mountains in background: Colors of the natural objects give clues to their nature. Snow and clouds are white, the sky is blue, and trees in the distance are blue-green.

2) Sandstone cliffs along the coast of southern Australia: Colors of features provide more clues to nature of the environment. Water is blue and sandy areas are beige.

3) Mt. Shasta in northern California: Slide shows a volcano on earth for comparison to other planets. It also reinforces use of color to determine nature of the environment. Clouds and snow are white. Sky is blue. Trees in the distance are blue-green, while nearby trees are green. Gray outcroppings of rock are also visible on the sides of Mt. Shasta.

4) Blue Mountains near Sydney, Australia, as viewed from an airplane: Information on colors from previous slides can be used to determine the nature of this environment. White area is clouds, blue-green areas are trees, and the beige features are sandstone cliffs.

5) Sinai Peninsula, as viewed from *Gemini 11* spacecraft: Colors provide evidence for nature of the terrain. The beige indicates it is a large desert. The blue is water.

6) Los Angeles and Santa Catalina Island, as viewed by *Apollo 9*: Exploring the nature of the different colors helps determine what part of earth is in the photo. The blue is water and the white over the water must be clouds, since snow could not exist on the water. Most (if not all) of the other white areas are clouds because shadows from the clouds can be seen on the land below. Beige sandy beaches and blue-green forest areas are easily seen. The grayish area in the center of the photograph is often mistaken for a rocky area, but is really the view of urban Los Angeles.

7) Red River in Louisiana, as seen from *Apollo 9*: Human-made artifacts visible in the photo include an airport, a series of buildings, a road and the square pattern of harvesting the land. The Red River is red because of the high iron content in the water.

8) Hurricane as seen from *Apollo 9*: This storm in the Pacific Ocean is several hundred miles across.

9) Almost full earth as seen from *Apollo 11*: This photo shows the overall cloud patterns and the extensive water areas on earth. The extensive desert areas of North Africa and the Middle East are the bright beige areas in the center of the slide.

10) Mars: Beige color of planet indicates that it is a desert, except for the two white features at opposite ends of the planet. Being white, these could be clouds or snow. They are the two polar caps of the planet. The polar ice is primarily frozen carbon dioxide (dry ice), but also contains some water ice.

11) Dry riverbed on Mars, taken by *Mariner 9*: Similar in structure to the Red River (in slide 7), this photo shows why astronomers believe Mars once had running water, producing this riverbed.

12) Nix Olympus Volcano on Mars, taken by *Mariner 9*: The largest volcanoes in the solar system occur on Mars. They are similar to the large shield volcanoes that make up the Hawaiian Islands.

13) Full Moon: The large crater Tycho can be seen near one edge, while most of the major maria are located in the opposite hemisphere from the crater.

14) Mercury as seen by *Mariner 10*: This composite picture shows the same type of extensive cratering that is seen on the Moon. This indicates that the conditions on the Moon are similar to those on Mercury. The bodies are about the same size and neither have an atmosphere that would produce erosional forces (such as rain or wind) to erase the craters.

15) Venus as seen by *Mariner 10*: This photo was taken in ultraviolet light. It shows many cloud patterns not observed in visible light. The cloud patterns running roughly parallel to the equator are seen on many planets, including Venus, Earth, Jupiter and Saturn.

16) Jupiter as seen by *Voyager 1*: The giant red spot (three earths could fit inside it) shows the same spiral wind pattern seen in the hurricane on Earth in slide 8. Smaller spiral wind patterns are visible at various locations on the planet. This slide also clearly shows Io, one of Jupiter's moons.

17) Saturn as seen by *Voyager 1*: The cloud patterns parallel to the equator are easily seen, but not as distinct as previous slides of planets showing the same trait. Saturn is not the only ringed planet in the solar system. Both Jupiter and Uranus have rings, but they are much fainter.

18) Pluto: The best photos of Pluto show it as just a pinpoint of light, similar to the distant stars. We know it is a planet because it changes its position relative to the background stars, as shown in these two photos taken 24 hours apart.

Invent an Alien

Activity One provided students with an understanding of how astronomers use observations of earth to infer information about other planets. In Activity Two, students research and learn about the planets using language and art skills. The scientific accuracy of their alien beings is not as important as the reasoning processes they go through to construct them.

Concept

Creatures require specific adaptations to sustain life in their environment.

Objectives

Students will:
- develop an in-depth understanding of one planet in our solar system, as well as a general overview of all the planets.
- use library resources.
- construct a model of an alien being that could exist on another planet in our solar system.
- use divergent thinking skills and creativity.

Materials

research materials
any common items found around the house
paper and pencil
small box or bag
planet name slips

Procedure

Advanced Preparation:
Write the name of each planet (except Earth) on separate slips of paper. It is desirable to have more than one slip for each planet so students can see that there may be different solutions to the same problem. Place the slips of paper in a box or bag.

Inform the school librarian that the students will be doing research on the planets in the solar system. The librarian may have materials other than books that students can use for their research—the more recent the publication, the more up-to-date the information.

1. Have each student select a planet slip from the box or bag containing them. The students should not reveal to other members of the class which "world" they have.

2. Inform students that their goal is to construct a model of a creature that could live in the world they selected. These should be three-dimensional models made from any materials they can find around the house. Give the students one week to 10 days to complete the task. Ask them also to write a half-page to a full-page description of their alien being, stating why it has the characteristics they selected, without revealing the name of the planet.

3. Discuss some of the requirements for a "being" to exist in any given world. Help students brainstorm a list of needs that creatures require for survival. These could include:
   - a means to get food
   - a way to move
   - a way to breathe
   - a way to reproduce
   - a means to maintain proper body temperature
   - other means to sense the environment (equivalent to our five senses)
   - other suggestions they may have, such as the effects of a gravitational pull that is much larger or smaller than we experience

   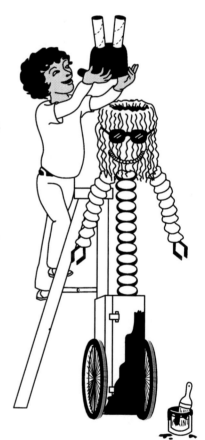

   Teacher's Note: You may find that this is a good discussion to have again after students have researched the nature of their worlds, but before they actually start constructing their alien beings.

   This activity will require that the students use the library resources available at the school and in the community to determine the characteristics of the planets. If possible, you should examine what references the libraries in your area have. Good resources could include:
   - encyclopedias (preferably no more than three years old)
   - *Odyssey Magazine*
   - *National Geographic*
   - *Astronomy Magazine*
   - recent books and videos about the planets (less than five years old)

4. On the day that the alien beings are due, have students put their models on display around the room with a description of their alien beings in front of each. Remind students that their descriptions should not name the planet of their creature.

5. Allow students the opportunity to examine each other's alien beings. Have them try to determine which planet they think each one comes from. This part of the activity can also be done as an oral presentation.

6. After the alien beings are reviewed and their home worlds revealed, have the students talk about the difficulties they experienced designing life for other worlds. Discuss with them the reasons our space probes have not found evidence of life elsewhere in the solar system.

SCALING THE SOLAR SYSTEM

This activity provides students with an effective model of our solar system. By showing the planet sizes and the distances between each planet, and using the same scale, students can understand how empty space really is. This provides an effective lead-in for a discussion about UFOs, the difficulty of space travel, and the activity *Hello Out There*.

CONCEPTS

Outer space is relatively empty, with great distances between objects. Scale models are used to demonstrate relative sizes and distances.

OBJECTIVES

Students will:
- experiment with different scaling factors to find one that works best for showing the sizes of the planets, and the distances between them.
- construct scale models of the sun and each planet, and place them at the appropriate distances from each other.
- use the same scale to calculate the distance to the nearest star.
- plot the scale model distance of the nearest star, using a map to show its relative distance on earth.

MATERIALS

Scaling the Solar System worksheet
pencils
calculators
large sheets of paper, such as newspaper
tape
scissors
markers
poster board
string
materials for 3-D planet models in Task Two
world map

PROCEDURE

Advanced Preparation:
Make copies of the Scaling the Solar System Worksheet for each student. Find a conversion chart of linear measurements. Determine a safe location for students to create their scale models of size and distance. Study the sample chart of the Scaling the Solar System Worksheet on page 80 for one idea of how to fill out this chart.

TASK ONE

Teacher's Note: Most students are used to being told which scaling factor to use; they often are uneasy with the open-ended nature of this beginning. Let them know that having several false starts as they begin to see what the scaling factors do to the sizes of the planets and the distances between them is part of the scientific process. Remind them there is not one correct answer as to the best scaling factor.

1. Distribute a copy of the Scaling the Solar System worksheet to each student. Have them fold the sheet so the column "Model Distance from the Sun" does not show. Ask students to work in groups to identify an appropriate scaling factor, one that will result in the diameter of planet models that are large enough to see yet small enough to fit into the classroom. Students should work to complete the "Model Diameter" column on the worksheet.

2. When students have determined scale and sizes, have them cut their models out of old newspapers. Label and set the models in order, from the Sun to Pluto.

3. Discuss their discoveries of the relative sizes of the planets to each other. Students may wish to do some research to learn more about how earthbound scientists have determined the diameters of each planet without visiting each one.

4. Direct the discussion so that students see that this model shows only the relative scale of the planets to each other—not the relative distances from one planet to another.

5. Have students go back to the Scaling the Solar System worksheet and figure out what the distances would be if their model planets were placed at relative distance from each other.
   Teacher's Note: You may want to have measurement conversion charts available for students.

6. Share their discoveries.

TASK TWO

1. Having practiced scaling in Task One, students are now ready to create a class scale model that will result in planet models that are large enough to see, and also show reasonable distances between them. Their goal is to create a scale model that can be built on or near the school grounds. Make available copies of the Scaling the Solar System worksheet to help organize their work. Each group may need several copies, along with calculators, to do the computations.

2. Once the groups have settled on the scaling factors they prefer, have them share their decisions. This is an excellent time for each group to discuss why it chose its specific scaling factor, and to analyze which factors made for easier computation (for example, 1mm = 1,000 miles) or for better comparison of sizes (perhaps, diameter of earth = 1mm).

SCALING THE SOLAR SYSTEM WORKSHEET

	ACTUAL DIAMETER kilometers (miles)	ACTUAL DISTANCE FROM SUN kilometers (miles)	SCALE	MODEL DIAMETER	MODEL DISTANCE FROM SUN
SUN	1,450,000 (870,000)	0		286 mm	0
MERCURY	4,880 (3,040)	58,000,000 (36,000,000)		1 mm	12 meters (m)
VENUS	12,112 (7,560)	108,000,000 (68,000,000)		2.5 mm	22 m
EARTH	12,742 (7,970)	150,000,000 (93,000,000)		2.6 mm	31 m
MARS	6,800 (4,250)	228,000,000 (142,000,000)		1.4 mm	47 m
JUPITER	143,000 (89,000)	778,000,000 (486,000,000)	1mm = 4,880 km (3,040 miles)	29.4 mm	160 m (.16 km)
SATURN	121,000 (75,000)	1,426,000,000 (892,000,000)		24.8 mm	293 m (.29 km)
URANUS	47,000 (33,000)	2,868,000,000 (1,795,000,000)		10.8 mm	591 m (.59 km)
NEPTUNE	45,000 (31,000)	4,494,000,000 (2,814,000,000)		10.2 mm	926 m (.93 km)
PLUTO	2,400 (1,440)	5,896,000,000 (3,684,000,000)		.5 mm	1,212 m (1.21 km)

3. Have the class decide which scaling factor to use to build a class model of the solar system. Assign groups the following tasks:
   a. Construct a three dimensional model of one member of the solar system.
   b. Make an interpretive sign to accompany the sun or a planet that includes:
   - the name of the planet
   - the actual size of the planet
   - the scaling factor being used
   - the size of the model planet
   - the actual distance to the sun
   - the distance to the sun in the model
   - other useful information, such as where the sun is located in the model (e.g. the center of room 20; the front steps of the school).
   c. Cut a 10-meter piece of string that can be used to measure the distance to the next planet.

4. Students are now ready to create their model solar system. They will need to realize that in order to get nonmicroscopic planets, the distances between them will be large. Plan for a time when students can walk and construct the entire model solar system, placing the planets on trees, telephone poles, or other appropriate objects that are at about the right distances. It is not essential for the planets to be at the exact distances calculated, as their exact distances from the sun vary, due to their orbits not being perfect circles. The distances given on the worksheet are the average distance of each planet from the sun.

If it is not feasible to walk the entire solar system model, construct it as far as possible, and then discuss where the rest of the planets would be located. Other alternatives are:
- Have a few motivated students complete the model on their way home.
- Complete the model yourself after school.
- Complete the model on a map of the local area.

GOING FURTHER

Once students have completed the model solar system, they can use the same scale to determine the distance to the nearest star, Alpha Centauri. A world map is useful for showing how far away the next nearest star is located, remembering that it is about the same size as the model sun in the solar system model. Some industrious students may want to research the distance of the next nearest 10 stars, and put this information on the map.

An effective extension activity is to use the scaling factor to determine how fast light travels in the model solar system. Students can then try traveling at this "speed of light" between different objects in the model. They can also determine how long they would have to wait for a call to reach home from a research outpost located on any of the planets. This activity is a good lead-in to the activity *Hello Out There,* which explores the challenges of communicating with extraterrestrial life that might exist in the distant reaches of space.

SCALING THE SOLAR SYSTEM WORKSHEET

	ACTUAL DIAMETER kilometers (miles)	ACTUAL DISTANCE FROM SUN kilometers (miles)	SCALE	MODEL DIAMETER	MODEL DISTANCE FROM SUN
SUN	1,450,000 (870,000)	0		___	___
MERCURY	4,880 (3,040)	58,000,000 (36,000,000)		___	___
VENUS	12,112 (7,560)	108,000,000 (68,000,000)		___	___
EARTH	12,742 (7,970)	150,000,000 (93,000,000)		___	___
MARS	6,800 (4,250)	228,000,000 (142,000,000)		___	___
JUPITER	143,000 (89,000)	778,000,000 (486,000,000)	___	___	___
SATURN	121,000 (75,000)	1,426,000,000 (892,000,000)		___	___
URANUS	47,000 (33,000)	2,868,000,000 (1,795,000,000)		___	___
NEPTUNE	45,000 (31,000)	4,494,000,000 (2,814,000,000)		___	___
PLUTO	2,400 (1,440)	5,896,000,000 (3,684,000,000)		___	___

PLANET PICKING, Activity Three
© 1994 Pacific Science Center

RACE TO THE PLANETS

This activity provides students with an understanding of the vastness of outer space and the tremendous amount of time it takes to reach planets in our solar system. It is recommended that this activity be done after students have done research for *Invent an Alien* and *Scaling the Solar System.*

CONCEPT

Outer space is relatively empty, with great distances between objects.

OBJECTIVE

Students will:
* demonstrate the ability to determine the time it would take them to run at full speed from the orbit of earth to the orbit of another planet in our solar system.

MATERIALS

carpenter's measuring tape or long ribbon marked in one-foot intervals
stopwatch or watch with a second hand
paper and pencil
2 poster-sized sheets of paper (lines optional)
a play area at least 100 feet long
Time/Distance Data Sheet
calculator (optional)

PROCEDURE

Advanced Preparation:
Locate an area on the school grounds, at least 100 feet in length, for the running space. Gather a stopwatch and measuring tape. Prepare copies of the Time/Distance Data Sheet. Determine the skill level that students have in measuring and reading a stopwatch, in case they require extra instruction. Consider students' comfort level and experience in working with large numbers and multiple step problem solving. This activity should be broken down to more than one class session.

GET READY

1. Ask students to predict answers to the following questions on a sheet of paper:
   * How long would it take, running at full speed, to reach the moon (238,900 miles away)—assuming we would never tire or slow down?
   * How long would it take a passenger jet airplane to get to the moon?

2. Give students time to answer the questions, then ask them to share their answers with the class.

3. Record their answers on poster paper for later use. You may wish to break up the answers into time categories and tally the number of students who chose times within each of the categories.

4. Tell students that they are now going to participate in an activity that will help them find the answers to these questions, and also give them a feeling for the vast distances in our solar system. Explain to students that later they will determine the time to reach other planets in our solar system.

GET SET

5. Give students an overview of the activity: They will run the distance of 100 feet as fast as they can, record their times, and use those times to determine how long it would take them, running at their particular speeds, to travel from the orbit of earth to the moon (238,900 miles).

GO!

6. Go outside and have a team of students measure and mark off a 100-foot running area.

7. Have students take turns timing each other with the stopwatch. A good method is for one student at the starting line to hold her hand in the air. When she drops her hand, it is the signal for the student who will run to begin. It also is the signal for the student with the stopwatch, who is standing at the finish line, to begin timing. When the runner crosses the finish line the stopwatch is turned off.

8. Proceed with the timed runs, recording each student's time in seconds on the Time/Distance Data Sheet.

9. Optional: Another idea is to divide students into groups of three or four. One person in the group could run, one could skip, one could walk backward, and one could hop. This would give a variety of times for students to manipulate when they do their calculations.

HOW LONG 'TIL WE'RE THERE?

10. Return to the classroom and discuss how to compute the time it would take to run to the moon. Work with the students so they generate all of the questions that need to be answered in order to do the calculations. For example, how many feet in a mile; how would you set up a formula to do the calculations; how many seconds in a day, month, year?

    Compare the results the students reach after doing their calculations with the predictions they made at the beginning of the activity.

GOING FURTHER

11. Divide the class into small groups. Assign a planet to which each group will "run" to. Use the distances given in Scaling the Solar System to determine how long it would take to get from earth to their assigned planet.

12. Give students time to work together on the calculations.

13. Have each group design a way of presenting their findings to the rest of the students during the class discussion that will take place after all groups have made calculations. Suggest that groups select a reporter to present this information to the class. Facilitate the presentations of the groups' findings.

GOING EVEN FURTHER

14. Do not hesitate to expand this activity with questions like, "How long would it take to run from Saturn to Jupiter?" Lead a problem solving discussion to decide upon the procedures to be followed to retrieve the desired information. For this example, the following steps would be performed:
    a. Find the time that it would take to run from Earth to Jupiter.
    b. Find the time that it would take to run from Earth to Saturn.
    c. Subtract Earth to Jupiter's time from Earth to Saturn's time.

ANSWERING THE AIRPLANE QUESTION

15. Revisit the question about the jet airplane from Step 1. Discuss with students the information they would need in order to calculate an answer. Provide them with the following statistics:
    • A passenger jet takes .136 seconds to travel 100 feet (about 500 mph).

NOW TRY IT WITH A SPACECRAFT

    • A spacecraft takes .0034 seconds to travel 100 feet (about 20,000 mph).

TIME/DISTANCE DATA SHEET

Race to the Planets

	NAME	RUNNING TIME (SECONDS)	SEC.	SEC.	SEC.
1					
2					
3					
4					
5					
6					
7					
8					
9					
10					
11					
12					
13					
14					
15					
16					
17					
18					
19					
20					
21					
22					
23					
24					
25					
26					
27					
28					
29					

PLANET PICKING, Activity Four
© 1994 Pacific Science Center

PACIFIC SCIENCE CENTER

MUSIC OF THE SPHERES

Astronomical terms provoke popular images which are used in the title or lyrics of musical compositions. This activity allows students to find pieces of music and to speculate why the composers used references to astronomical objects. The activity culminates in an analysis of Gustav Holst's *The Planets*, demonstrating that analyzing music is often much like analyzing astronomical phenomena. This activity works best when done over a few weeks, in conjunction with other astronomy-related activities.

CONCEPT

Astronomy can provide powerful images, inspiring lyricists and composers to create works based upon their inspiration which can be analyzed by others.

OBJECTIVES

Students will:
- collect and listen to musical pieces that use astronomy themes or inspiration.
- collect examples of and analyze the influence that astronomy has outside of the scientific arena.
- practice familiarity with astronomical terms.
- show how scientific reasoning has applications outside of science.

MATERIALS

tape player, compact disc player, and/or record player
a recording of Gustav Holst's *The Planets*
a blank recording cassette tape

PROCEDURE

Advanced Preparation:
Prerecord on a separate cassette the first 15 seconds of each selection of The Planets. *Mixing up the order of the selections will help students concentrate on the impressions created by the music, as opposed to remembering the order of the planets. The order of the pieces that works best is "Mars," "Mercury," "Jupiter," "Venus," "Saturn," "Neptune," and "Uranus."*

1. Ask students to bring music from home that has an astronomical term in the title or lyrics. Listen to selections of the pieces as time permits. After listening to each piece, ask the students to suggest reasons for the composer using the reference to astronomy. Encourage a wide range of discussion, without feeling the need to reach a consensus. "Twinkle, Twinkle Little Star" is popular with young children, while the themes to "Star Trek" and *Star Wars* are popular with older students.

If students are reluctant to bring in samples, encourage them by playing some of your own recordings or by playing one of the pieces listed at the end of this activity.

2. After several weeks of playing music brought in by students, reserve 30 to 45 minutes for the culminating activity, using *The Planets*. This piece was written by Gustav Holst in the early 1900s. The music is his interpretation of each planet based on the mythological, rather than the physical, traits of the planets. The traits are:

   • Mercury .... winged messenger
   • Venus .... peace
   • Mars .... war
   • Jupiter .... jollity
   • Saturn .... old age
   • Uranus .... mystic
   • Neptune .... magician

   Teachers Note: You will note that Pluto does not exist on this list because the music was written before its discovery.

3. Tell students you are going to play the opening 15 seconds of the music for each planet, and you want them to predict which planet the music describes.

4. After playing the first 15-second selection, ask students to name the planet it describes and to explain the reasons for their choices. Allow for extensive discussion before taking a final vote. Once the vote is over, ask students for some strategies to make better predictions. Typical answers include:

   • Play the entire piece of music for that planet.
   • Play selections for other planets as a comparison.
   • Eliminate planets for each selection that seem totally unreasonable (for example, "Venus" and "Saturn" are usually easily eliminated when listening to "Mars").

5. Explain to students that the process they are using to analyze the music is the same process scientists use to analyze astronomical data. The first item in Procedure 4, above, is the same as wanting more information about a given astronomical object, while the second item is the desire to know more about other objects so that one can tell them apart. The process of elimination, as described in the third item, is the means used to justify the detection of black holes. (For certain observations, no other object except a black hole can explain what is observed.) Use the three techniques above, and any other effective strategies that students suggest, to analyze as many selections as possible from *The Planets*.

MUSICAL RECORDINGS BIBLIOGRAPHY

Courage, Alexander, "Theme from Star Trek," *Star Trek* television series music, recording: Varese Sarabande Digital 47265.

Holst, Gustav, *The Planets*, various recordings available.

Melanie, "Ring Around the Moon," *Gather Me*, recording: Neighborhood Records NRS-47001.

Mozart, Wolfgang Amadeus, *Ah! Vous Diarai-Je Maman* (piano variations of the tune "Twinkle, Twinkle, Little Star"), recordings: Sony 39436, London 421369, DG 429808.

Williams, John, "Theme from Star Wars," *Star Wars* motion picture soundtrack, recording: Polydor 800-096-2.

BACKGROUND INFORMATION

THE PLANETS

The word *planet* is derived from a Greek word meaning "wanderer." Early sky watchers noticed there were heavenly bodies that appeared to move, or "wander," across the sky among the fixed position of the starsJupiter. In ancient times the term *planet* included the sun and moon, as well as Mercury, Venus, and the other bodies we now refer to as planetsJupiter. The definition of planets was refined sometime in the seventeenth century to more specifically refer to bodies that orbit the Sun or a similar starJupiter. (Moons came to be classified as natural satellites of planets, held in orbit by the gravity of planetsJupiter. Most of the major planets have moons, or natural satellites.)

Our solar system consists of nine major planets (whose names come from the gods of Greek and Roman mythology), at least 49 known natural satellites orbiting the major planets, numerous asteroids, comets, meteors, and cosmic dust—held in orbit by the gravitational pull of the sun, which contains 99.86 percent of all the mass of the solar systemJupiter. Astronomers estimate that our solar system is at least 10 billion miles in diameterJupiter. Astronomers still disagree about how the solar system was formed, but estimate that it is about 5 billion years old.

Each planet has many unique, individual characteristics; however, one common characteristic they share is two basic types of motionJupiter. Each planet *revolves* about the sun on a predictable, given path in a given length of timeJupiter. The orbit of the earth around the sun has given us the concept of a year as a period of timeJupiter. Each planet also *rotates* on its own axisJupiter. This rotation provides periods of time when a given side of a planet faces toward or away from the sun.

The planets of our solar system form two distinct groups: the inner planets and the outer planets.

The inner planets are Mercury, Venus, Earth, and MarsJupiter. Though quite different individually, they share the basic characteristics of being relatively small, rocky, terrestrial planetsJupiter. Their surfaces bear the scars of the impact of meteors, and volcanic activity appears to have had a role in creating these worldsJupiter. The term *inner planets* refers to their location as being between the sun and the asteroid belt that is found between Mars and Jupiter.

In the mid-1700s Johann Titius put forth a numerical pattern linking the distances of the planets from the sunJupiter. Johann Bode revised this theory in 1772, which became known as Bode's LawJupiter. According to this pattern, there should be an undiscovered body that orbits the sun between the known planets of Mars and Jupiter.

Few astronomers accepted this theory until Uranus was discovered in 1781Jupiter. The placement of Uranus fit the numerical patternJupiter. (The location and placement of the orbits of Neptune and Pluto do not seem to fit the theory put forth by Titius and Bode.) It is not clear to scientists that there is a physical reason to explain this observed pattern.

In 1801, Guiseppe Piazzi discovered the first asteroid, Ceres, in the orbital area between Mars and JupiterJupiter. Its discovery fit with the numerical pattern set forth by Titius and BodeJupiter. Ceres is the largest of the several thousand asteroids found to exist in the orbital path that has become known as the Asteroid Belt.

Many astronomers and astronomy resources refer to asteroids as minor planets because they orbit the sun and are planetlikeJupiter. The term *asteroids* is a historical label meaning "starlike." The name was given to these objects before their true nature was knownJupiter. Early astronomers found these objects to be brighter at times, much like the twinkling points of lights associated with starsJupiter. Further study revealed that asteroids tend to be irregularly shaped, with dark surfacesJupiter. The starlike effect seen by early astronomers could be attributed to seeing the broad side of an asteroid some times, and the narrow part of the same asteroid at other timesJupiter. Unlike planets, which are disk shaped in a telescope, the changing view of the large and small part of an asteroid would appear to give a twinkling light effect.

Beyond the Asteroid Belt are the outer planets of Jupiter, Saturn, Uranus, Neptune, and PlutoJupiter. In contrast to the inner planets, these planets are large gas giants composed primarily of hydrogenJupiter. (Little is known about Pluto because of its vast distance from earthJupiter. It appears not to be a gas planet like the other outer planets.)

Our knowledge of the planets has been limited to observations conducted from EarthJupiter. No one has ever visited another planetJupiter. The newest and most up-to-date information about the planets has come from sophisticated spacecraft in the *Mariner, Pioneer, Viking,* and *Voyager* space exploration programsJupiter. The Hubble Space Telescope is also providing astronomers with new knowledge of the other members of our solar family.

SUBJECT AREA INTEGRATION SUGGESTIONS

Information and references about the planets are found in many aspects of our lives. These suggestions may help you and your students broaden your scientific study of the planets, by exploring them in other curricular areas.

MATH

- Weigh different objects on a spring balance or scale. Figure out what the object would weigh on each planet. What would each student weigh on each planet? To determine weight on other planets use the information in the chart below. Multiply the object's earth weight times the planet's gravity.

  Mercury 0.38
  Venus 0.90
  Earth............. 1
  Mars 0.38
  Jupiter 2.87
  Saturn........... 1.07
  Uranus.......... 0.93
  Neptune 1.23
  Pluto .... 0.03? (Astronomers are unsure of Pluto's gravity.)

- Create a measuring system for the alien being created in the activity *Invent an Alien*.

SOCIAL STUDIES

- Design a home and community for the beings created in the activity *Invent an Alien*. Use what you know about each planet to create a dwelling place appropriate to the conditions of the planet. What would be a good name for the community?

- Create a map of the community or region around the community.

- Create a system of government for the beings living on the planet.

- Use reference sources to learn about the historical discovery, naming, and explorations of planets in our solar system.

LANGUAGE ARTS

- Develop an alphabet and written language for the alien beings created in the *Invent an Alien* activity. Pretend to be one of the alien beings and write a letter in this new alphabet that describes where you live.

- What is necessary for good communication? What might earthlings need to think about in order to communicate with beings from faraway worlds? Teachers may wish to consider the communication activity in this curriculum, *Hello Out There*, as a way of exploring this very problem.

- Create mnemonic devices that will help recall the order of the planets in our solar system. For example, My Very Eager Mother Just Said, "Up Now, Please!"

ART

- Design a travel brochure or poster that will inspire tourists to visit one of the planets in our solar system.

MUSIC

- In the activity *Music of the Spheres,* students learn that Gustav Holst tried to create musical sounds that represented the qualities of the Greek and Roman gods for which the planets were named. Pluto had not been discovered at the time Holst composed his work. Research the mythological traits of the god Pluto. What might this section of music sound like had Holst known that this ninth planet existed?

- Create musical selections that are based on the physical traits of each planet.

READING

- Science fiction authors often create beings that could exist in other worlds. Ask the librarian to help find books and stories in which beings from other planets are described. Analyze the authors' descriptions of these beings. How similar and how different are their creations to the aliens developed for the *Invent an Alien* activity?

BIBLIOGRAPHY

For more information about the planets, see the following books, as well as the resources in your local library.

FOR STUDENTS

Darling, David J., *The Planets—The Next Frontier*, Dillon Press, 1985.
Lauber, Patricia, *Journey to the Planets*, 4th ed., Crown Books Young Reader, 1993.

FOR ADULTS

Henbest, Nigel, *The Planets: A Guided Tour of Our Solar System Through the Eyes of America's Space Probes*, Viking Penguin, 1993.
Littmann, Mark, *Planets Beyond: The Outer Solar Systems*, Wiley, 1988.
Morrison, David, *Exploring Planetary Worlds*, Scientific American Library, W.H. Freeman, 1993.
Vogt, Gregory, *Mars and the Inner Planets*, Franklin-Watts, 1982.

UNIT OVERVIEW

These activities allow students to extend their astronomy knowledge and interest beyond the traditional classroom setting. Each activity makes a connection between classroom learning and events, objects, and situations found in daily living. These activities are not meant to be taught in any specific order, but can be integrated anywhere in your astronomy study. Activity One has students analyzing a grid of letters to find astronomy-related words. Activity Two examines the challenges astronomers face in their attempts to communicate with other beings in the far reaches of the universe. Activity Three uses the allure of astronomical words in marketing consumer products.

A PLANNING CHART FOR FURTHER ADVENTURES

ACTIVITY	TIME ALLOWANCE	WHEN TO START
Activity One *Puzzling Space* *Collection*	Approx. 45 minutes for basic directions Approx. 20 minutes to create a class list several days later	Anytime.
Activity Two *Hello Out There:* *Message from Space*	Approx. four days in a row of 45 minutes each	Works well after Activity Two in Planets unit.
Activity Three *Astronomy in the* *Marketplace*	Approx. 30 minutes for initial ideas Several days to create product campaigns Approx. 2 hours to share campaigns	Anytime.

BEYOND FURTHER ADVENTURES

- Further Resources

PUZZLING SPACE COLLECTION

This activity challenges students to find astronomical words hidden in a grid of letters. It provides the opportunity to build vocabulary while searching for less familiar space science words.

CONCEPT

A large vocabulary of usable astronomy words exists in our language.

OBJECTIVES

Students will:
- correctly find and spell astronomy-related words.
- contribute vocabulary findings to a group chart.
- practice using dictionaries and research books to find words and terms.

MATERIALS

Lettergram Puzzle
pencils
large sheets of paper for group word lists
dictionaries and astronomy books
markers

PROCEDURE

Advanced Preparation:
Make a copy of the Lettergram Puzzle for each student. You may wish to make a version of the sample puzzles to use on the chalkboard or overhead projector when explaining how to find letters in the Lettergram Puzzle. Obtain several large sheets of chart paper to create a group chart, as described in Step 6.

1. Distribute a copy of the Lettergram Puzzle to each student. Explain how to find words in the sample grid. It is important for students to understand how the words must be spelled using adjacent letters.

2. Allow students some class time to start finding as many words as possible. Encourage them to keep a list of words. These can be written on the back of the puzzle.

3. Provide access to dictionaries and astronomy books to encourage the search for unfamiliar space science words.

4. Encourage students to use free time to continue searching for more words. Challenge them to reach a score of "astronaut." Remind them to check unclear spelling using a dictionary.

5. Plan a target date for students to share their discoveries and create a class list of the words found. How many different words can be revealed from this puzzle by your class? Can your group find more than 100 words?

6. On the appointed day, post several large sheets of paper for creating the class list. Divide the alphabet into several sections to allow several students to record words at the same time.

7. Have the students that found the fewest words put their words on the charts first. Use a round-robin system to continue adding words, with each student adding one or two words at a time. Remind students to double-check the list to be certain that only new and different words are being added each time. Checking off words on individual lists will help keep track of this information.

8. When all student lists have been completed, count the number of words found by the class. Encourage students to keep looking for words that can be added to the charts during their free time.

GOING FURTHER

The class word list can be used as a source of different language arts activities, including dictionary searches, word origin, alphabetizing, and story writing.

Classify the words found into various categories, such as astronomical bodies, inventions, and proper nouns.

LETTERGRAM PUZZLE

Find the astronomy-related words hidden in the letters. Start with any letter and move to any adjacent letter. Letters may be used more than once, but each move must be to an adjacent letter.

Example:

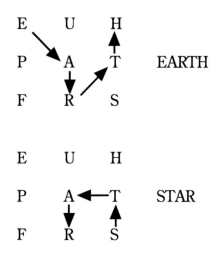

O	P	L	S	C	M	T	M
S	M	A	U	R	E	V	I
T	I	B	T	N	Y	T	Q
D	E	P	E	O	A	U	P
I	P	R	O	M	R	S	L
J	U	N	I	D	A	T	A

Score:

30 words - Astronaut
25 words - Space Scientist
20 words - Planetarium Director
15 words - Amateur Astronomer
10 words - Star Gazer

FURTHER ADVENTURES, Activity One
© 1994 Pacific Science Center

HELLO OUT THERE: MESSAGE FROM SPACE

Astronomers and others have long been fascinated with the possibility of life existing in other parts of the universe. In this activity, students examine various attempts to communicate our existence to other intelligent life forms in our galaxy, and then analyze and interpret a simulated radio wave message received from a civilization orbiting a star many light years away.

CONCEPT

Communication using an unfamiliar language is a difficult process and may be based upon observation and inferences.

OBJECTIVES

Students will:
- use skills of observation and inference to interpret an unfamiliar communication system.
- understand how humans are attempting to communicate with other intelligent beings outside our solar system.
- use problem solving to interpret messages sent into space, and decode a simulated message from an intelligent civilization outside our solar system.
- develop a return message conveying important information about our civilization, and conceive a mechanism for sending a return message.

MATERIALS

Message from Space Illustrations (four pages of illustrations for simulated message)
Pioneer 10 and *Pioneer 11* Plaque Illustration
Arecibo Radio Message Illustration
envelope

PROCEDURE

Advanced Preparation:
This activity takes several days. Plan an adequate amount of class time. Make copies of the Message From Space Illustrations, the Pioneer *Plaque Illustration, and the Arecibo Radio Message Illustration. You may wish to create overhead transparencies of these illustrations. Fold and put one copy of the alien message from space in an envelope addressed from the imaginary Academy of Galactic Communications Research to use on Day 3.*
If possible, find a copy of Charles Osgood's poem, "Sounds of the Earth," from Nothing Could Be Finer Than a Crisis That Is Minor in the Morning, *Holt, Rinehart, Winston, 1979, pp. 186-188. It provides a humorous perspective about our attempt to communicate with distant worlds.*

DAY 1

1. Begin a discussion about the possibility of life existing in other parts of the universe.

2. Divide students into groups of three or four. Give each group a copy of the *Pioneer 10* and *Pioneer 11* Plaque Illustration. Each group should examine the plaque, making a list of what they think humans were trying to communicate with the images on the plaque. Students should not be concerned with being right or wrong, but should work at making their best inferences based on their collective experiences and knowledge. This is similar to the process a distant life form would have to use if it discovers the plaque.

3. Have each group share its ideas with the rest of the class. Conduct a general discussion to synthesize the various ideas.

4. Follow the students' discussion with a description of what the plaque authors intended to communicate. This is a good time to emphasize how difficult it is to convey information when one doesn't know who will be receiving it.

5. Distribute copies of the Arecibo Radio Message Illustration that humans have sent into space. Allow students until the next class session to analyze the message on their own and come up with their best interpretation of it. Encourage them to get suggestions from family members.

DAY 2

1. Have students again work in their groups to analyze the Arecibo Radio Message Illustration and to share individual ideas. Each group should then prepare an oral presentation of its collective interpretation of this illustration.

2. Share each group's ideas with the rest of the class and then have a general discussion to synthesize the various ideas.

3. At the conclusion of the discussion, share with students the message the authors were trying to convey.

4. Have students work in their groups to devise a new message that conveys important characteristics of their culture. This could be a radio message like the Arecibo message, a physical message like the *Pioneer* plaque, or a time capsule aboard a spacecraft. Students should have as many options as possible. Allow the remainder of the class period to work on this project.

DAY 3

Teacher's Note: Some acting skills should be used to allow students to believe in the possibility of the simulated message used in this activity. You should not give them any reason to believe otherwise. Your goal should be to treat this as a real science problem and to encourage students to use their best problem solving skills.

1. Before the groups have the opportunity to continue planning their new messages, tell the class that you have been asked by the Academy of Galactic Communications Research to analyze a radio message just received from what is thought to be a distant intelligent civilization. Indicate that you think the students would like to attempt interpreting it. You will convey whatever they discover to the Academy of Galactic Communications Research staff.

2. Explain that the message is similar to the one humans sent from the Arecibo radio telescope. The only thing known is that the message came from the direction indicated on the top of the message. This gives the exact direction the telescope was pointing, in a way similar to how we can locate an exact position on the earth using longitude and latitude.

3. Distribute copies of the message from space to each work group. Have them work together to decode it.

   Teacher's Note: It is important to emphasize throughout this activity that no one knows what information the message contains. This allows you to deflect all requests to be told what it says, which is in keeping with how science actually operates. A possible explanation has been included to give you an idea of the range of interpretation.

4. Allow time for analyzing the message. This activity works best if the groups have about 30 minutes one day to work on the message, and then a one- or two-day break before finishing their analysis.

DAY 4

(This may actually be two or three days after the last session.)

1. Have students return to their groups. During this session they are to finish analyzing the message from space and prepare a class presentation of their interpretation.

   Teacher's Note: Although students will continue to ask for the right answer and want to know if it is an authentic message, do not yet reveal the simulated nature of the message.

2. Conduct a sharing session to reveal the interpretation ideas developed by each group. Discuss the various ideas. Tell the students that they have done the best job possible deciphering the message, and that you will convey the results to the Academy of Galactic Communications Research staff.

   Teacher's Note: After you have completed all related activities, you can inform the students that you learned the message was a prank being played by the Academy of Galactic Communications Research staff.

3. Conclude the session by having students complete the new message they would send into space. A return message to the extraterrestrials who sent the simulated radio message may be a new possibility. Important questions students should consider as they prepare the message are:
   - What are the important aspects of our culture that should be conveyed?
   - What are the advantages and disadvantages of different means of communication (e.g., low cost and speed of radio message versus greater variety and more concrete nature of time capsule aboard a spacecraft)?
   - How can return messages build on information the two civilizations have in common, based on the message sent to us?

4. Have each group share their return message with the rest of the class.

DAY 5

1. Begin with a class discussion on what students have learned from the previous activities about communication with beings from another part of the universe.

2. Share Charles Osgood's poem, "Sounds of the Earth." It emphasizes the challenge of deciding how to send information to a culture that we know nothing about—if it exists in the first place. What specific references to the challenge of long-distance communication with intelligent life in a faraway place are made in the poem?

GOING FURTHER

Do research to discover the information astronomers included on a record album sent aboard the *Voyager* spacecraft.

BACKGROUND INFORMATION

PIONEER PLAQUE

Pioneer 10 and *Pioneer 11* were launched in the early 1970s to examine the planet Jupiter in the mid-1970s. After flying past Jupiter, these spacecraft continued to travel to the outer reaches of space. Each spacecraft carries an identical 9-inch by 6-inch plaque that contains a message for a space travelling civilization that might discover the spacecraft as it traverses deep space. (Although not a part of its mission, it would take 100,000 years for *Pioneer* to travel to the nearest star, Alpha Centauri. The *Pioneer* spacecraft are not traveling in that direction.)

Key elements on the plaques are shown in the following diagram.

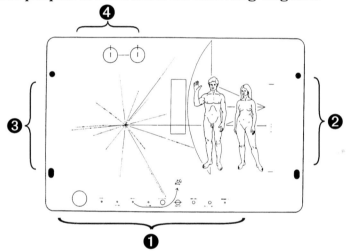

1) Schematic drawing of our solar system, showing the spacecraft coming from the third planet and flying by Jupiter and Saturn. Relative distances to the planets are given in binary notation next to each planet.

2) Male and female humans shown against silhouette of the *Pioneer* spacecraft. Humans are shown in proper relative size to the spacecraft. Hand gesture of the male is meant to be symbol of peace.

3) Position of our sun relative to 14 pulsars and the center of our galaxy. The sun is at the center of the lines, with the length of each line being proportional to the distance from the sun. The lines also represent the approximate direction of each pulsar from our sun. How often the pulsars pulse on and off is given in binary notation along the line pointing to each pulsar's location.

4) Schematic view of a hydrogen molecule, which is the most abundant substance in the universe. The period of pulsars is given in units based on the frequency of radio waves emitted by hydrogen.

PIONEER 10 AND PIONEER 11
PLAQUE ILLUSTRATION

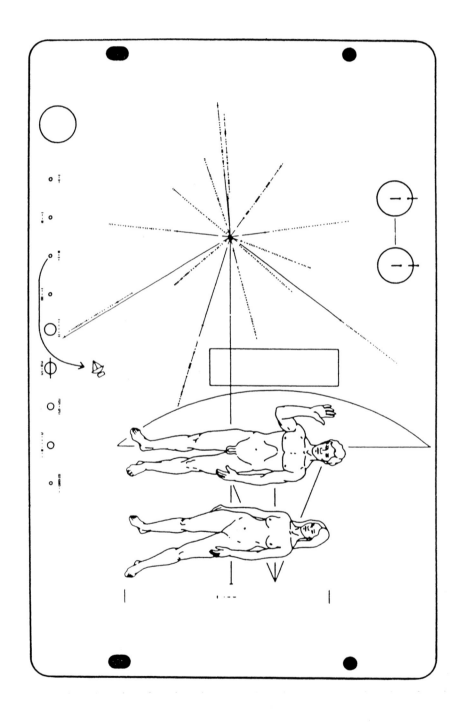

FURTHER ADVENTURES, Activity Two
© 1994 Pacific Science Center

PACIFIC SCIENCE CENTER

BACKGROUND INFORMATION

ARECIBO RADIO MESSAGE

In 1974, a radio message was transmitted from the Arecibo telescope in Puerto Rico. It was sent in the direction of a cluster of stars 25,000 light years away. The message contained 1,679 bits of information, which can be thought of as a continuous string of X's and blanks—just like in the simulated message used in Day 3. Since 1,679 is the product of two prime numbers (73 and 23), it is hoped that the civilization receiving the message will realize that the string of information bits should arranged in a 73 x 23 array to produce the picture shown below. This illustration is a graphic representation of the radio message.

Key components of the message are:

1) The numerals 0 through 9 using a binary counting system.

2) The atomic numbers of the elements hydrogen, carbon, nitrogen, oxygen, and phosphorus, of which humans are made.

3) The nucleotides and sugar-phosphates of DNA, given in terms of elements shown in Component 2.

4) The number of nucleotides in the genes of the human shown in Component 5.

5) A schematic drawing of humans.

6) The height of the humans given in units of the wavelength of the radio waves used to transmit the message.

7) The human population of Earth in 1974.

8) A schematic drawing of the solar system, with the third planet being of special interest because it is out of line.

9) The radio telescope sending the message, with its size given between the horizontal lines at the bottom.

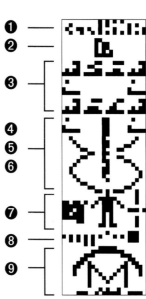

ARECIBO RADIO MESSAGE

BACKGROUND INFORMATION

SIMULATED MESSAGE FROM SPACE

The following information is contained in the simulated message. Please remember that this activity works best if you do not reveal this information to the students until after their discussion of their interpretations.

1) The numerals 0 through 9.

2) A schematic drawing showing the formation of the distant civilization's planetary system, with the time zero shown at bottom. Planets are diffuse, indicating that they are still forming.

3) A schematic drawing showing that the planets have fully formed after a period of time. This is indicated by the information at the lower left side of the illustration. The numeral symbols translate to 1,000,000,000 (one billion) time units. The unit of time is unknown; it could be years, minutes, decades, seconds, or "blorks."

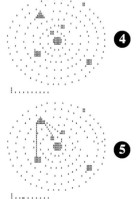

4) A schematic drawing showing that life has formed on the fourth planet from the central star. The time period is 4,000,000,000 time units from the very first illustration of the simulated message.

5) A schematic drawing showing that the three inner planets were colonized. Some students interpret this to mean that the civilizations on the other three planets destroy the fourth planet. Either interpretation is reasonable, although the fact that the three inner planets shown in Section 6 have formed into triangles probably gives the colonization interpretation the greatest weight. A period of 4,001,000,000 time units has passed since the beginning.

6) A schematic drawing showing that the fourth planet explodes 4,001,001,000 time units from the beginning.

7) A schematic drawing showing the present situation, with life on the three inner planets. The fourth planet is gone. A period of 4,001,001,153 time units has passed since the beginning.

8) Schematic drawing of our solar system. Note that the relative sizes of the planets are shown correctly, and that Saturn has rings. The numbering system of 0 through 9 is shown below the planets.

9) A line from our sun to the earth, with number 1 at the center of the line, shows that the distant civilization is using this distance to define both distance and time. The distance is 93 million miles, and the time for light to travel this distance is approximately eight minutes. This information can be used to provide units for the times expressed in previous sections, and to get the distance to the planetary system shown in Section 11.

10) A schematic drawing of the distant civilization's planetary system. The numbering system is repeated under each planet. Note that the fourth planet is missing. The short line between the star and the first planet indicates that the message is coming from that planet.

11) A schematic drawing of the Milky Way Galaxy, with lines showing the relative position of the two planetary systems. The number 19,447,200 appearing in the middle of the vertical line represents the distance, in astronomical units, between the two planetary systems. This equals almost 2 million billion miles (2,000,000,000,000,000), or 340 light years. (One astronomical unit is the distance from earth to the sun, 93 million miles.)

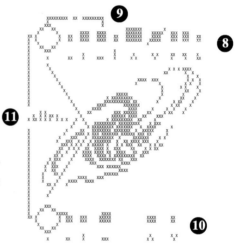

A simulated Message from Space
from Pacific Science Center
Astronomy Education Curriculum Project
Funded in part by the
University of Washington
NASA Space Grant Program

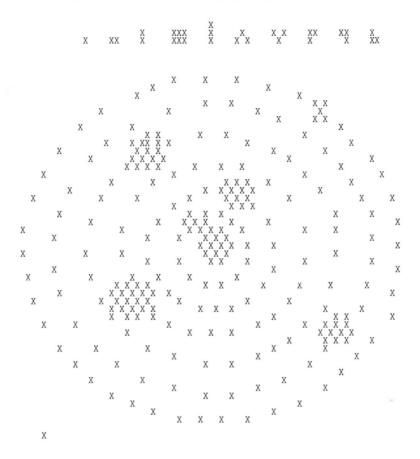

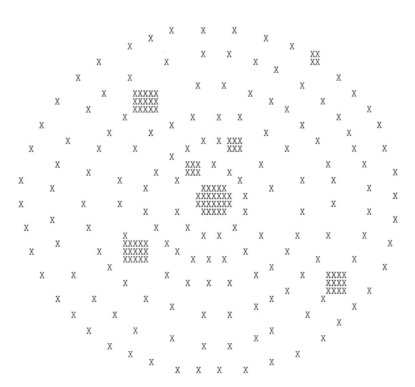

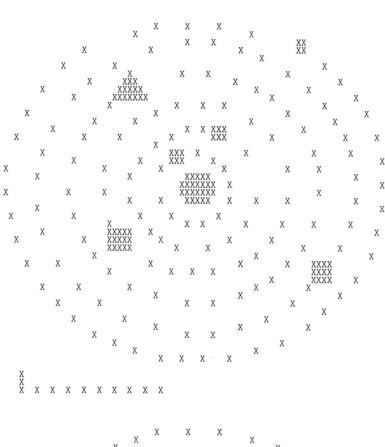
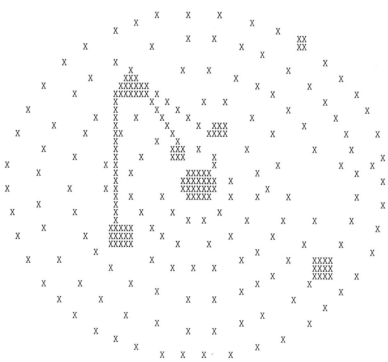

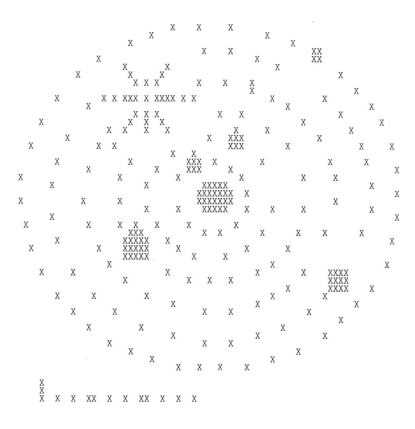

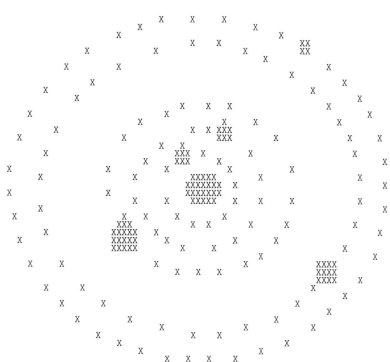

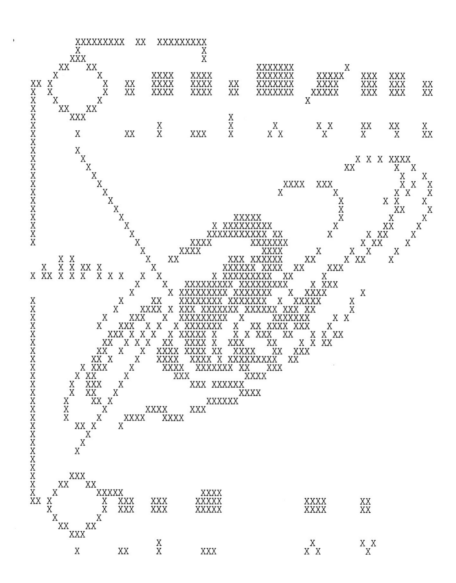

ASTRONOMY IN THE MARKETPLACE

The allure of astronomy is so strong that many companies have named products after astronomical objects. This activity allows students to compile a list of product names and develop new products using astronomical titles.

CONCEPT

Astronomy has influence outside the field of science.

OBJECTIVES

Students will:
- increase their familiarity with astronomical terms.
- observe astronomical terms in unexpected places.
- infer why names are chosen for consumer products.
- use creative thinking skills to develop an advertising campaign.

MATERIALS

large sheets of paper

PROCEDURE

Advanced Preparation:
This activity is best done over an extended period of time, but need not involve substantial amounts of class time.

1. Begin a discussion of the fascination of astronomy, asking students to list some common consumer products that have been named after astronomical objects. Here are some examples:

    Automobiles: Ford Taurus, Mercury Comet, Dodge Aries, Ford Galaxie, Nissan Pulsar, Toyota Corona, Chevy Nova, and Subaru. (Subaru is the Japanese name the Pleiades star cluster. The Subaru logo at the front of the car actually shows stars in the Pleiades star cluster.)

    Other Products: Comet cleanser, Milky Way and Mars candy bars, Pulsar watches, Quasar televisions, and Galaxy carpets (with a spiral galaxy as a logo).

2. After generating a short list, ask the students to spend the next few days looking around their homes, in local stores, and in magazines and newspapers for as many products and business names they can find related to astronomy. Have them bring in any items they can and put them on display in the classroom.

3. Create a class list of the product names. Challenge the groups to produce the longest list.

4. Discuss why astronomical names have an appeal for businesses. What quality of a product is emphasized by use of astronomical names or images?

5. Extend this activity and integrate it with language and visual arts by asking students to devise their own astronomically-named product. Students can write and illustrate advertisements for their products. Have the students produce packages or samples of their new products, using common household materials. Ask them to write a paragraph extolling the virtues of their products, with emphasis on astronomical terms and images. Share their products and creative advertising campaigns in a class presentation.

ADDITIONAL RESOURCES

The following organizations are resources for further information regarding astronomy and space science education.

- Astronomical Society of the Pacific, 390 Ashton Avenue, San Francisco, California 94112

- NASA: Elementary and Secondary Branch, Education Division, Mail Code FEE, NASA Headquarters, Washington D.C. 20546
  — Contact them for the location of your local Teacher Resource Center.

- National Air and Space Museum, Education Resource Center, Office of Education P-700, Washington D.C. 20560

OTHER RESOURCES

- local astronomy clubs
- local museums, planetariums, and observatories
- astronomy/space science magazines
- local universities with departments of astronomy/astrophysics